CW00434309

The Portrait

Sponsored by **Enterprise Oil**

John Hayes

in British Art

Masterpieces bought with the help of the National Art Collections Fund

National Portrait Gallery

Published for the exhibition at the National Portrait Gallery,
London from 8 November 1991 to 9 February 1992

Published by National Portrait Gallery Publications,
National Portrait Gallery, 2 St Martin's Place,
London WC2H OHE, England, 1991

ISBN 1 85514 050 0 (cloth)
ISBN 1 85514 051 9 (paperback)

A catalogue record for this book is available from the British Library

House editor: Gillian Forrester
Assistant editor: Denny Hemming
Designer: Derek Birdsall RDI
Indexer: Helen Baz

Phototypeset in Monophoto Van Dijck by Servis Filmsetting Limited,
Longsight, Manchester, England
Printed in England by BAS Printers, Over Wallop, Hampshire
Cloth edition bound by Hunter & Foulis Limited
Paperback edition bound by W.H. Ware & Sons Limited

Photographic acknowledgements

The exhibition organizers would like to thank the following for making
copyright photographs available. All other photographs were supplied by
the owners of the works of art reproduced or the sources given in the text:

By gracious permission of Her Majesty The Queen Fig. 24, pp. 36, 44, 52,
128; Agnew's p. 168; Wendy Baron p. 148; copyright Canterbury Museums
p. 133; Colnaghi's p. 104; Courtauld Institute of Art Figs. 12, 27, pp. 42
(left), 108, 118; Kenneth Garlick (photo copyright Agnew's) Fig. 8;
copyright Vivien John pp. 165, 166; Paul Mellon Centre for Studies in
British Art Fig. 6, pp. 58 (copyright National Museum of Wales), 92, 122,
126; National Museum of Wales Fig. 29; Royal Commission on the
Historical Monuments of England (copyright Warburg Institute) p. 84;
Tate Gallery, London Fig. 9, p. 66.

Front cover: *Aubrey Beardsley* by Walter Richard Sickert, 1894 (detail; no.
56). Reproduced by kind permission of the Tate Gallery, London. ©.
Back cover: *Arthur Capel, 1st Baron Capel, and his Family* by Cornelius
Johnson, *c.* 1641 (no. 7). National Portrait Gallery, London ©.

Contents

Enterprise Oil is more than usually delighted to be sponsoring *The Portrait in British Art*, a celebration of British portraiture spanning nearly four centuries of artistic achievement unique in Western art. The National Portrait Gallery has assembled, from all over Britain, a most remarkable collection of portraits, featuring sitters from all walks of life and reflecting the changing nature of British society from the brashness of the Elizabethans to the aftermath of the First World War.

This exhibition, together with its scholarly and beautifully produced catalogue, serves two purposes. It informs us about a tradition in British art which is still in a flourishing state today. And it demonstrates the role played by the National Art Collections Fund, Britain's leading art charity, in saving countless portraits which are part of our national heritage for generations of Britons, and our friends from overseas, to enjoy forever in the public art galleries not only of London but throughout Great Britain.

Graham Hearne CBE
Chairman and Chief Executive
Enterprise Oil plc

Preface

This exhibition explores one of the most popular aspects of British painting. The British seem always to have had a fascination for recording themselves, and this exhibition brings together contrasts in motivation, personality and technique over 400 years. They range from a dashing fantasy of Shakespeare as national hero, to the intimacy of Millais's portrait of his wife. There is something here to stimulate and surprise every visitor.

But *The Portrait in British Art* has a subtext, and that is the National Art Collections Fund. All the works of art in this exhibition have been acquired with the help of the NACF. We are very proud to see the fruits of our work brought together and housed so magnificently by our hosts at the National Portrait Gallery. Our sincere thanks must also go to Enterprise Oil, whose generosity has made this exhibition possible.

The work of the National Art Collections Fund has been central to public collecting ever since our foundation in 1903. These portraits in some part demonstrate the range of our work, coming as they do from all over the country, and including treasures from national and local museums. But in subject matter this is a tiny corner of our work: we help to buy paintings, sculpture and decorative art from all ages and nations. In fact our criteria are simply quality and relevance to the museum.

The National Art Collections Fund's work is a lifeline to museums and galleries collecting for the future. We rely on the support of our growing membership for our effectiveness. I very much hope that you will enjoy the paintings in this exhibition, and that they will inspire you to join us as a member. In doing so you will be helping to ensure the future quality of museums and galleries all over the country.

Sir Nicholas Goodison
Chairman
National Art Collections Fund

Foreword

The National Art Collections Fund is a peculiarly British institution, founded, like many a Victorian charitable organization, to promote the public good by private subscription. Over the Channel in France works of art sought by the national collections are acquired by the State as a matter of course; French cultural institutions have benefited from a long history of pride and political concern for the *patrimoine*. Across the Atlantic in the United States the situation is the opposite. Museum purchases are normally made with private money, funds often being generated by their Trustees, and it is not at all uncommon, before a purchase is initiated, for curators to approach benefactors known to be interested in specific fields. Characteristically, the British way of doing things is a complex combination of both systems. The national museums and galleries receive annual purchase grants (unfortunately frozen since 1983), while the State also provides funds for the acquisition of works in lieu of inheritance tax and under the aegis of the National Heritage Memorial Fund. But additional and substantial private funding remains essential if British museums and galleries are to continue to augment their collections with any degree of seriousness. At the start of my directorship I organized what proved to be a long and arduous public appeal to save the superb Reynolds portrait of Laurence Sterne (no. 29 in the exhibition). The NACF's contribution was a cornerstone of the campaign, as it has been (and is) for other museums in similar circumstances. To a very considerable extent, in fact, private support for museum purchases in Britain is channelled through the National Art Collections Fund, whose membership and purchasing power have grown out of all recognition in the last ten years or so.

Since its foundation in 1903 the NACF has supported well over one hundred purchases by the National Portrait Gallery, a most remarkable record. It is entirely fitting, therefore, that we should offer hospitality for the latest in a series of NACF exhibitions designed to increase public awareness of its sterling work. The Trustees and I welcomed with enthusiasm the NACF's initial proposal of an exhibition devoted to British portraiture, and Carole Patey conducted the negotiations leading to sponsorship with her usual efficiency and success. Sir Nicholas Goodison and Sir Peter Wakefield, respectively Chairman and Director of the Fund, have been immensely supportive throughout the preparation of the exhibition; and their colleagues, notably Robert McPherson, who put together the first lists, have been endlessly helpful in supplying pertinent information.

Curators and registrars of all the museums who have so generously lent paintings have provided much valuable material for the catalogue and if, as explained in the note, only the more important references have been incorporated into the entries, the completed loan forms have been indispensable as a starting point for research. My colleagues, Malcolm Rogers and Jonathan Franklin, have assisted over particular problems, and supplied the translations for the Latin inscriptions in the Souch portrait of Sir Thomas Aston and his family. In preparing the catalogue and its introduction, I have been indebted to the research and writings of many scholars in the field of British art, and it is a pleasure to acknowledge in particular Quentin Bell, Dennis Farr, Kenneth McConkey, Sir Oliver Millar, the late Sir David Piper, Professor Marcia Pointon, Desmond Shawe-Taylor, Sir Roy Strong, and the late Sir Ellis Waterhouse, all of whom have written perceptive books, essays and catalogues, several of them substantial histories dealing with different periods of British art; alas, there is as yet no Pelican history of British nineteenth-century painting.

Gillian Forrester has edited the catalogue with her customary energy and care, cheerfully sacrificing much of her own time to ensure its accuracy. In the course of this work she and Julia King have chased up much recalcitrant but significant detail. Denny Hemming has edited my text with great common sense, and I have been happy to accept nearly all her excellent suggestions for improvement. I am greatly indebted, as always, to Derek Birdsall for his professional skills as designer and for his sensitivity and imagination in arranging the material. The Tate Gallery has very kindly allowed us to use its Sickert portrait of Aubrey Beardsley for the jacket, and the Watford Museum has similarly allowed the use of its Herkomer portrait of Anna Herkomer for poster and leaflet.

Without the readiness of so many museums and galleries throughout Britain to lend important portraits to the exhibition – we were gratified that there were so few refusals – it would not have been possible to mount so comprehensive a display of British portraiture in honour of the NACF. I thank in particular the Trustees of the National Gallery, who kindly agreed to lend three great masterpieces; the Trustees of the Tate Gallery, who lent no fewer than seven pictures; and Richard Green, the Director of York City Art Gallery, who has been especially helpful concerning the great double portrait by Cotes with its elaborate and delicate frame. The heavy responsibility of handling the loans and their transport has been undertaken with customary aplomb by Kathleen Soriano. Richard Hallas has coped at short notice with much additional work in the frame shop. Finally, and certainly not least, the exhibition itself has been admirably planned and designed by Caroline Brown.

We have been especially fortunate with the help we have received so unstintingly from all quarters. But major exhibitions nowadays cannot subsist on kindness; they depend upon substantial financial assistance. Without the generosity of Enterprise Oil the exhibition could never have taken place. The Trustees and I are immensely grateful to Graham Hearne and his colleagues for their enlightened sponsorship.

John Hayes
Director
National Portrait Gallery
2 October 1991

The National Portrait Gallery would like to thank the following who contributed in many different ways to the organization of the exhibition and preparation of the catalogue:

Brian Allen
The Duke of Atholl
Wendy Baron
Victoria Barwell
BAS Printers
J. Susan Bourne
Ann Bukantas
Lady Juliet de Chair
The Viscount Cowdray
Heather Cummins
Jacqueline Dugas
Judy Egerton
The Lord Egremont
Elizabeth Einberg
Elizabeth Foy
Kenneth Garlick
The Marquess of Hertford
Mary Hinds
Marilyn Hunt
William Joll
Susanna Kerr
Cecily Langdale
Barbara Milner
Evelyn Newby
Helen Sainsbury
Servis Filmsetting Limited
Gyongyi Smee
Tracey Walker
Norma Watt
G.M. Wilson
Sarah Wimbush
The Viscount Windsor
Selina Woodruff
Caroline Worthington

List of Lenders

Introduction

I: *The Mainsprings of Patronage*

Fig. 1
Hans Holbein: *Christina of Denmark, Duchess of Milan*
c. 1540
Oil and tempera on panel, 179 × 82.5 (70½ × 32½)
National Gallery, London

For much of its recent history England has been a less centralized country than its continental neighbours; but London, and, certainly under the Tudors and Stuarts, the court, has always been the centre of artistic patronage and the source of style. The splendid medieval tombs of the great and the knightly scattered throughout English cathedrals and churches, increasingly likenesses of individuals, are one of the glories of its heritage; but the history of portraiture in Britain does not begin in earnest until the age of Henry VIII, who attracted numerous foreign artists and craftsmen to his court in connection with the building of his palaces of Whitehall, Hampton Court and Nonesuch. Surprisingly, perhaps, Hans Holbein, a great decorative artist, was not among these men. When he came to London, 1526–1528, it was with an introduction from Erasmus to Sir Thomas More, for whom he painted a large and magnificent family group (destroyed in the eighteenth century: copy by Rowland Lockey in the National Portrait Gallery). At the start of his second and longer stay in England, 1532–1543, only terminated by his death, Holbein was patronized by the German Steelyard merchants. Not until 1536 did he work for the king. Then he executed the great dynastic wall painting for the Privy Chamber at Whitehall (destroyed by fire, 1698), part of the cartoon for which survives in the National Portrait Gallery. His work at court included the production of portraits of Henry's prospective brides, a visit to Brussels in 1538 resulting in one of his masterpieces, the full-length of Christina of Denmark (Fig. 1).

The Renaissance flavour of Henry's court was not revived by Elizabeth. Indeed the Virgin Queen was positively insular. Federigo Zuccaro was the only really important painter to visit England during her reign; he arrived in 1575, with an introduction probably to the Earl of Leicester, to be of service to the queen, but only remained for six months at most. Who, then, were the painters who flourished at her court? Steven van der Meulen, an able Flemish artist, was pre-eminent in the 1560s; George Gower was the most fashionable painter of the 1570s and 1580s and became Serjeant Painter to the Queen in 1581; Marcus Gheeraerts the Younger was the favourite of the 1590s, executing probably in 1592 his celebrated portrait of Queen Elizabeth, magnificently attired and bejewelled, standing firmly on the English portion of a globe with her feet on Sir Henry Lee's home at Ditchley (Fig. 2).

James I's son, Henry, who became Prince of Wales in 1610, had the same international aspirations and passion for building as Henry VIII. The young prince was loyal to Robert Peake, who had been appointed his Principal Painter when he was nine, but he employed neither Gheeraerts (no. 1) nor William Larkin (Fig. 3), the best English portraitists of the decade, whom he regarded as too old-fashioned in their outlook; instead, he tried hard to persuade Michiel van Miereveld, the Prince of Orange's portrait painter, to cross the Channel. He was unsuccessful, and what Sir Roy Strong has called 'England's lost Renaissance'[1] perished with his untimely death in 1612. Henry's artistic tastes and determination to bring London within the orbit of contemporary European culture were amply shared by his brother Charles who, before his accession to the throne in 1625, had sat to Velázquez and employed Miereveld's pupil, Daniel Mytens, in his service. Orazio Gentileschi came to London in 1626, Gerard van Honthorst in 1628, and Rubens in 1629. Early in 1632 Van Dyck, who had been in London for a few months in the winter of 1620–1621, arrived in England. Charles was determined that this time he should stay. He established him in a house at Blackfriars, gave him an annual retainer of 200 pounds, and, on 5 July, knighted him. It was Van Dyck who immortalized the brittle structure of the Caroline court.

Peter Lely succeeded to the mantle of Van Dyck at the court of Charles II but, although he was highly esteemed and lived in considerable luxury to demonstrate his social standing, he was not actually knighted until the last year of his life, 1680. Godfrey Kneller, well-organized and self-assured, the first professional artist in Britain to aspire to be a country gentleman, held a similarly undisputed position as the leading painter of his age for almost twice as long as Lely (Fig. 4). He was Principal Painter not only to William III, who knighted him, but also to Queen Anne and George I, who made him a baronet in 1715. He was then widely held to be superior to Van Dyck, and the longevity of his place at the top is illustrated by the well-known story of the painter, John Ellys, who, on coming to see Reynolds in his early days, objected to his work so vehemently that he burst out in a rage 'Shakespeare in poetry, and Kneller in painting, damme!'[2]

Both Lely and Kneller were painters of the fashionable world which revolved round the court rather than artists attached to the monarch, carrying out a royal policy, as Holbein and Prince Henry's entourage had largely been. Yet the total lack of interest in the visual arts shown by both George I and George II created something of a vacuum at the centre of artistic life. Grandees of Charles I's time such as Buckingham (Fig. 3) and Arundel had always been independent patrons, but now patronage became more widespread. George Vertue wrote in 1737 that 'several noblemen have their particular. painter or favourite which is wholly at their promotion – and recommendation as particularly. yᵉ Earl of Burlington. [see no. 13], who has prompted and supported Mʳ Kent'.[3] At the same time, a number of foreign portraitists, of whom the most successful was Jean Baptiste van Loo (Fig. 5), seized the opportunity to wrest what

Fig. 2
Marcus Gheeraerts the Younger: *Queen Elizabeth I*
c. 1592
Oil on panel, 241.3 × 152.4 (95 × 60)
National Portrait Gallery, London

Fig. 3
William Larkin: *George Villiers, 1st Duke of Buckingham*
c. 1616
Oil on canvas, 205.7 × 119.4 (81 × 47)
National Portrait Gallery, London

Fig. 4
Sir Godfrey Kneller: *Sir Christopher Wren*
1711
Oil on canvas, 124.5 × 100.3 (49 × 39½)
National Portrait Gallery, London

2

3

4

business they could from Kneller's distinctly mediocre successors; while George II's eldest son, Frederick, Prince of Wales, held an opposition court at Leicester House, employing artists of the Rococo avant-garde. Frederick was a genuine connoisseur and an avid collector as well as a patron, and his untimely death in 1751 was a disaster for the arts in England.

Joshua Reynolds, who was in Italy when Frederick died, returned to England in 1753 with a new, classically inspired, programme for revivifying British portraiture but no royal patron to promote it. A more stable centre of patronage was needed, and the artists of the day sought it in public display; imitating the French Salon they proposed to hold annual exhibitions of their work. In April 1760, a few months before the death of George II and the accession of his twenty-two-year-old grandson George III, the first exhibition of the Incorporated Society of Artists of Great Britain was held in London. In this very miscellaneous show 178 works were shown by 68 artists. The Society's successor, the Royal Academy, founded in 1768, was able to build on secure foundations and, vigorously led by Reynolds, its first President, effectively replaced the court as the centre of patronage and the arbiter of taste. Only the Prince Regent, later George IV, with his passion for portraiture, was to equal the influence of his Academy in this field. It was a remarkable achievement. Elections to the coveted rank of Academician became fiercely competitive; and there is good evidence, for example, that Reynolds excluded George Romney from the initial list of forty out of professional jealousy.[4]

The Academy exhibitions, in which for over fifty years portraits predominated, were both a market-place and a showcase (Fig. 6). Reynolds regularly exhibited the finest and most characteristic of his portraits, and for a century and a half the annual exhibition, which connoisseurs and patrons accepted as the touchstone of all that was best in British art, was the essential means by which an artist remained in the public eye and underpinned a successful career. Even those at the head of the profession ignored the Academy at their peril. Allan Ramsay's reputation was affected adversely by his

Fig. 5
Jean Baptiste van Loo: *Sir James Burrow*
1737
Oil on canvas, 127 × 101.6 (50 × 40)
The Royal Society, London

Fig. 6
Pietro Martini (after J. H. Ramberg):
The Royal Academy Exhibition of 1787 [Somerset House]
Engraving

reluctance to exhibit. In February 1803, two months before the opening of the annual exhibition, Thomas Lawrence told his friend and mentor, Joseph Farington, that he proposed to 'decline exhibiting this year as He had many small pictures to finish'. Farington's reply was firm: 'I told him I thought no policy of that kind shd. prevent his exhibiting. He must keep his name before the world.'[5]

Inevitably the competitiveness of the occasion, exacerbated by the crowded nature of the hang, favoured the production of full-lengths, pictures that could not escape notice; and painters might well use stronger tones or more glaring colours for the period of the exhibition, adjusting their work subsequently. Gainsborough complained in 1766 that there was 'a false taste and an impudent stile prevailing, which if Vandyke was living would put him out of countenance';[6] nonetheless, only a few years later, probably in 1772, we find him writing to a client: 'I think we could still finish a little higher, to great advantage ... I am fired with the thoughts of Mrs Pulteney's giving me leave to send you to the Royal Exhibition, and of making a good Portrait of you' (Fig. 7).[7] Martin Archer Shee, who succeeded Lawrence as President of the Academy, said that Gainsborough 'often painted higher for the room, and afterwards brought his pictures down'.[8] In the late 1790s Lawrence was attracting attention by painting on a preternaturally large scale; he exhibited his huge portrait of Kemble as Coriolanus in 1798. The following year he caused consternation among his fellow portrait painters by submitting a colossal full-length of a Miss Jennings (Fig. 8); William Beechey in particular was bitter about it, and said 'if He had seen it before He sent his pictures, He wd. only have sent his portrait of Lord Cornwallis' and not his female portraits, pleading with Farington that a 'rule must be made that if portrait painters paint pictures larger than life, – they must not therefore command *center places*'.[9]

Reviewing was then in its infancy, and rival newspapers promoted their favourite painters: Gainsborough, for example, was 'puffed' and his current work continually noticed in the *Morning Herald*, owned

Fig. 7
Thomas Gainsborough: *William Johnstone Pulteney, later 5th Baronet*
c. 1772
Oil on canvas, 237.5 × 149.8 (93½ × 59)
Yale Center for British Art, Paul Mellon Collection

Fig. 8
Sir Thomas Lawrence: *Elizabeth Jennings*
(later Mrs William Lock II)
1799
Oil on canvas, 238.8 × 142.2 (94 × 56)
Private Collection
This photograph was taken before the portrait was cut down to
127 × 101.6 cm (50 × 40 inches) in about 1912.

by his friend, Henry Bate-Dudley, while he was taken to task for superficiality in the *Public Advertiser*. More serious criticism began with Hazlitt and the leisurely columns of the fortnightly or monthly magazine; a mid-Victorian newspaper might cover the Academy in eight or ten issues. Throughout the nineteenth century, criticism could affect careers for better or worse. F.G. Stephens was an able and staunch defender of Millais when he needed it most, in the late 1850s. Whistler, on the other hand, suffered badly from newspaper critics: 'They prevented my getting commissions: they would have killed me if they could'.[10]

Early in the Academy's history appointment as Principal Painter to the monarch or the Prince of Wales became more of an honour than a serious factor in the pursuit of a career; Reynolds was determined to secure the royal appointment on the death of Ramsay in 1784 more as a matter of pride, as President of the *Royal* Academy, than anything else, for, as he wrote afterwards: 'The place which I have the honour of holding, of the King's principal painter, is a place of not so much profit, and of near equal dignity with His Majesty's rat catcher. The salary is £38 per annum, and for every whole length I am to be paid £50, instead of £200 which I have from everybody else'.[11] Lawrence and John Hoppner pursued their rivalry for the favour of the public in the 1790s and 1800s principally on the walls of the Academy. Their offices as Principal Painter to the King and the Prince of Wales respectively were significant chiefly because they polarized their positions in rival political and social factions, Lawrence securing commissions from the Tory Establishment, Hoppner from the Whigs and the Carlton House set. In 1818 Lawrence was asked by the Prince Regent to travel to the international conference at Aix-la-Chapelle and paint for the nation the Allied heads of state and military leaders responsible for the downfall of Napoleon, not because of his royal appointment, but because he was the outstanding painter of the age.

David Wilkie succeeded Lawrence as Principal Painter to the King in 1830 and he was retained in the post by Queen Victoria, but after his death the position dwindled in importance even in the royal estimation. The Queen was enchanted by Landseer and Winterhalter, who held no official positions; and Winterhalter was more truly a court painter, never seeking patronage outside the royal circle, than any artist working in England since Van Dyck. Since then state portraits and pictures of ceremonial events have been executed by artists selected as any patron might commission work. Luke Fildes, for example, was invited on the advice of the President of the Academy to paint the state portrait of Edward VII (Fildes said he would be 'expected to superintend and pass' the numerous replicas required).[12]

At the same time, by the late Victorian period the Royal Academy was losing its standing among progressive artists – though not with the public, with whom the commissions lay. 'Bevies of duchesses, yards of satin, acres of lace and gentle English landscape scenes populated by cows which . . . would have felt it indelicate to produce milk' was how Quentin Bell castigated the years between 1890 and 1914.[13] Numerous, increasingly radical, counter exhibiting bodies began to spring up, starting in 1877 with the Grosvenor Gallery, where the opening exhibition was dominated by James McNeill Whistler and Edward Burne-Jones, and followed in 1886 by the New English Art Club, of which John Singer Sargent and Wilson Steer were founder members. The fount of patronage was becoming increasingly diverse, and the art dealer of far greater importance as an intermediary, though it should be remembered, England being England, that one third of those who contributed to the first exhibition of the New English Art Club later became Academicians, and the Club itself more and more conservative. As Kenneth McConkey has written, in the years leading up to 1914 the Academy, the International Society and all the other annual exhibitions were displaying 'consensus portraiture'.[14]

II: *Patron & Painter*

Fig. 9
Joseph Wright of Derby: *Sir Richard Arkwright*
1789–1790
Oil on canvas, 241.3 × 152.4 (95 × 60)
Private Collection

If the mainsprings of patronage as far as portraiture is concerned were, first, the Tudor and Stuart courts and court circles, later the public exhibition – a transference from a broadly autocratic to broadly competitive criteria which has been fundamental to the development of British portraiture – the demand for portraits has been widespread since at least the eighteenth century, when the Swiss miniaturist, André Rouquet, who worked in London for thirty years, 1722–1752, confessed himself amazed at 'how fond the English are of having their pictures drawn', adding, by way of explanation, that 'peoples fortunes are more upon a level in England than in any other country'.[15] The luxury trades flourished in London to an extent found nowhere else in Europe.

Some people's fortunes were very great by any standards, and family portraits played a supporting role with their newly built or rebuilt mansions and their parks and estates in asserting their dynastic importance and their position in local affairs. In Tudor times sets of kings and queens and portraits of national dignitaries were acquired in addition to family portraits for the adornment of long galleries; and copies of portraits of monarchs, prime ministers, famous writers and, of course, relatives and friends, continued to be commissioned for country house collections. Allan Ramsay, as Principal Painter to the King, supplied endless full-lengths of George III and Queen Charlotte. Both Gainsborough and Hoppner had to paint numerous copies of their portraits of William Pitt; Nollekens made innumerable replicas of his busts of Pitt and Charles James Fox. But the family portraits were the core of these collections. What were the prerequisites for these works? Likeness was all-important to most patrons; after all, portraits were primarily commemorative, a matter of record, and it was for this reason that the nobility and upper echelons of the gentry commissioned portraits of their houses and their animals, notably favourite or race-winning horses. But, since they were also dynastic props, portraits had to dignify and flatter. Many of Reynolds's sitters look arrogant, and no doubt they were. Lawrence and Sargent gave them glamour. Hubert von Herkomer, however, voiced the views of most painters in the matter when he wrote that 'It is merely common justice to humanity that you should take some pains to catch a sitter at his best'.[16] A fascinating glimpse of local rivalry is to be found in the letters John Michael Wright wrote to his patron, Sir Walter Bagot, of Blithfield, Staffordshire: 'Yo^r frames . . . are richer then the first patterne I shewed yow . . . but my Lady Wilbraham comming hither caused her's to bee made broader and richer . . . wch occasioned that I did the like to all yo^{rs} that they might not bee inferiour to any in that Country.'[17]

In the eighteenth century many first-generation merchants or industrialists were satisfied with unadorned realism, and they got it in the portraits of Wright of Derby and Mason Chamberlin. By the Victorian age the same classes, self-confident and powerful, wanted to be seen as prominent members of society, prospective landowners, indeed entrants to the House of Lords; they did not want to be portrayed, as Sir Richard Arkwright had been, and as doctors, scientists and engineers still were, with the attributes of their calling, or specific symbols of their rise to fame, beside them (Fig. 9). Lawrence painted a splendidly dramatic group portrait of Sir Francis Baring, the banker, in conclave at the bank; significantly, it was not Sir Francis, but his sons, who objected to the publication of a mezzotint of this picture because they did 'not like to have their Father exhibited with a *Ledger* before him'[18] (Fig. 10).

Since, as Marcia Pointon has pointed out, portraiture was a buyer's market, certainly by 1780, when there were over 100 portrait painters trying to make a living in London alone,[19] patrons could afford to be high-handed and expected to be treated deferentially: Sir Francis Bourgeois once remarked, perhaps because it was exceptional, that Gainsborough, who 'knew his own value ... maintained an importance with his sitters, such as neither Beechey or Hoppner can preserve'.[20] There were no formal contracts and, if painters in such demand as Lawrence in his later days often took years to complete a routine portrait (having taken a half payment at the outset), patrons were also liable to default: Northcote recalled of Reynolds that 'In a small room next to his own painting room, there were a great number of those portraits which had been rejected and were left upon his hands'.[21] Normally at this period a portrait would be delivered within a year or less of the first sitting.

Most wealthy people, if they did not live in London, had their portraits painted in the metropolis, when they were up for the parliamentary session or social season, or simply on a visit. In the eighteenth century Bath also had a season, and sitting for one's portrait was a recognized way of filling in the time between Pump Room and masquerade; William Hoare, who was primarily a pastellist, working for the less affluent as well as the fashionable, spent his life there, and Gainsborough had his studio in Bath for fifteen years. Few major artists settled in other centres, as Wright of Derby chose to do; Henry Raeburn was the first great Scottish painter to remain in Edinburgh, tempted as he was for a moment to come south after Hoppner's death in 1810. Nonetheless, by the eighteenth century there was clearly a nationwide demand for portraits amongst those classes of society with any pretensions to gentility.

As early as the 1630s John Souch was producing quite elaborate portraits in Chester (Fig. 11); and, in those days of slow and difficult travel, there must have been many provincial artists active all over England who were prepared, like the young Gainsborough, to stay in a country town and turn their hand to 'every kind of painting'.[22] Sir Oliver Millar, from his researches in the seventeenth-century records of the Painter-Stainers' Company and elsewhere, has spoken of 'the disturbing number of names of painters whom we know to have been at work [men such as 'John Gybbes Picture maker dewelling At Canterburye'], but to whom no single piece can be attributed with certainty'.[23]

Thomas Hudson travelled widely in the 1730s, and as late as 1742 (when Reynolds was apprenticed in his studio) Vertue noted his 'lately going in to the Country for some months has met with great encouragement – by painting many pictures in so Small a time. 50 or 60'.[24] Gainsborough worked in his native Suffolk as a young man, principally painting head-and-shoulders portraits of the local gentry and members of the professional classes, lawyers and clergymen (no. 27). But, although he kept his prices down to eight guineas for a head and fifteen for a half-length (a good deal less than Hudson or Reynolds operating in London) and was personally very popular, he found, after eight or nine years in practice there, that commissions were becoming scarcer even in this reasonably prosperous part of the country. 'I thank you, Sir,' he wrote to an attorney in Colchester in 1757, 'for your kind invitation of procuring me a few Heads to paint when I come over', and, a year later, 'I thought I should have been at Colchester by this time ... but business comes in, and being chiefly in the Face way, I'm afraid to put people off when they are in the mind to sit'.[25] Romney, who was trained by the Kendal painter, Christopher Steele, worked for a time in that town; and George Stubbs, as a young man, travelled about the north country as a portraitist. The advent of photography in the early years of Queen Victoria's reign did nothing to curb the multiplying acreage of portrait painting, because by then the painter was supplying a kind of image (or status symbol) framed in gilt which the photographer was unable to imitate; but it killed the miniature, with its microscopic attention to likeness.

Very little is known about the way Elizabethan painters managed their practice, although it is clear from his remarks that Nicholas Hilliard maintained a pleasant and extensive painting room. Van Dyck, who was trained in one of the largest, busiest and most competent studios in Europe, that of Rubens, knew very well what it took to survive as an international painter of the front rank. Although London was not Antwerp, and he had few pictures on his order books other than portraits, he was under constant pressure, especially in the last years of his life, and must have run a well-organized studio at Blackfriars; presumably he employed several assistants for his style to have been so widely, if generally rather

10

11

incompetently, disseminated in the twenty years after his death in 1640. His practice was to set down his ideas for a new portrait, from the life, on 'a little piece of blue paper'; the design would then be marked out on the canvas by assistants; the head itself would be painted by Van Dyck, and most of the costume and accessories completed by the studio. Sir John Suckling describes the master 'with all his fine colours and Pensills about him, his Frame, and right Light, and every thing in order'.[26] He followed Titian, Lucas Cranach, Anthonis Mor and Rubens in comporting himself like a *grand seigneur*. Lely, equally the gentleman, seems to have been haughty when he chose, a 'mighty proud man ... full of state',[27] Pepys called him, noticing with surprise on one visit 'in what pomp his table was laid for himself to go to dinner';[28] J.M. Wright's commission to paint the series of full-lengths of judges for Guildhall arose from Lely's refusal to travel to the City to carry out work. Kneller was even more pretentious, and was widely ridiculed for it; yet he was perhaps the grandest of all the Stuart painters, ending up with a country establishment and as a deputy lieutenant for Middlesex.

Van Dyck, Lely and Kneller were all on equal terms with their patrons, and no doubt charged them accordingly; Wright was properly critical of the system when he wrote in 1676: 'I have begun ... diverse ladyes, who are all sufficiently satisfied and judge mee moderat comparatively to Mr Lilly'.[29] As early as the 1660s, Lely was using drapery assistants, even in his most important commissions. In 1666 Pepys 'saw the heads, some finished and all begun, of the Flaggmen in the late great fight with the Duke of Yorke [later James II] against the Dutch';[30] not all these were completed by Lely himself. Later Lely had a large number of assistants, of whom the best known are John Greenhill and William Wissing; their task, like those who had served Van Dyck, was to complete canvases on which Lely had painted the head, in many cases according to stock patterns available for selection by the sitter. Lely even had postures, which were numbered, prepared in advance; amongst the canvases left in his studio at the time he died were 'Whole length postures No.8 & 1. and 1. cloth[es] and hand on it'.[31] Not surprisingly 'all his pictures had an Air one of another ... So that Mr Walker yc Painter swore Lilly's Pictures was all Brothers & sisters'.[32] Wright, too, had assistants, as we learn from his correspondence with Sir Walter Bagot: 'had I been byass't by Interest, yor peices had beene sent yow long before now finish't up by my workemen, but, upon the faith of a Christian, I reserve them to bee done by my owne hands.'[33] Kneller presided over a workshop even more efficiently run than that of Lely. As Sir Oliver Millar has written: 'His team of specialized assistants could cover a large area of canvas in a very short time under his supervision; and the portraits which poured from his establishments rarely fall below a sound and workmanlike level.'[34]

By the mid eighteenth century drapery assistants as well paid as Joseph van Aken and Peter Toms were almost regarded as artists in their own right. Of Van Aken Vertue wrote that 'for severall portrait painters he designd & composd their disposition of pictures in a much better and more Ellegant Manner then they coud most of them'.[35] Hudson, one of the principal painters for whom Van Aken worked (Fig. 12), ran the busiest studio in London at this time, and was able to charge the highest rate for an apprentice; as Ellen Miles has written, he may have worked primarily as a craftsman, but he lived like a gentleman.[36] Like Lely and Kneller, Hudson had a variety

Fig. 10
Sir Thomas Lawrence: *Sir Francis Baring, Bt, John Baring and Charles Wall*
c. 1807
Oil on canvas, 154.9 × 226.1 (61 × 89)
Baring Brothers & Co., Ltd, London

Fig. 11
John Souch: *Unidentified Marriage Portrait*
c. 1640
Oil on canvas, 102.2 × 126.3 (40¼ × 49¾)
Grosvenor Museum, Chester

Fig. 12
Thomas Hudson: *Mary Panton, Duchess of Ancaster*
1757
Oil on canvas, 234 × 132 (92 × 52)
Grimsthorpe and Drummond Castle Trust, Lincolnshire

of stock poses, and thought it perfectly natural to produce portraits of women not only in the same posture but with identical costume and jewellery. Reynolds, who had a portfolio of prints from which sitters might select a posture that appealed to them, was the last British portrait painter to run a studio on the scale of Kneller or Hudson. In the next generation, Lawrence, as his work-load increased, had the top floor of his house converted for the use of several assistants, but, like Gainsborough (who employed only one assistant), he was psychologically committed to painting all the portraits he cared about with his own hands – and indeed, his glittering bravura style did not lend itself as readily to the workshop system as did the more generalized canvases of Hudson or Reynolds.

Portrait painters' studios were popular rendezvous and had to be stylish and well-appointed. From quite early in his career the impecunious Lawrence maintained grand painting rooms, 'supporting a certain Manner in a Gentlemanly Profession and obliged to deal with Fashion and its thousand whims'.[37] When Beechey took a house in Harley Street in 1803 he thought it essential, if he was to maintain his position in the profession, to 'expend £1000 more in building painting and shew rooms'.[38] Reynolds, too, had spent far more than he could afford when, in 1761, he bought 'a handsome house on the west side of [Leicester Fields]; to which he added a splendid gallery for the exhibition of his works, and a commodious and elegant room for his sitters'.[39] He even gave a ball to mark the opening of his gallery to the public. But Reynolds was well aware of the need for promotional skills. In 1753, on his return from Rome, he had painted a dramatic full-length of his friend Commodore Keppel (Fig. 13) to hang in his studio as an advertisement of his abilities. Conscious that the fame, status or beauty of a sitter were the crucial elements in the acclaim of a portrait he had sent a full-length of the Duchess of Hamilton (one of the beautiful Gunning sisters) to the first Society of Artists' exhibition in 1760 (see p. 100). And he made sure that all his finest works were widely known from engravings. In a later age Philip de Laszlo offered to paint important sitters free of charge in order to further his career. The fashionable Victorian portrait painters all built grand houses for themselves, notably in Fitzjohn's Avenue, Hampstead and Melbury Road, Kensington; and, although their studios were no longer meeting-places, they impressed their sitters with painting-rooms that looked more like drawing-rooms than places of work. At the same time, as a result of the nineteenth-century belief in artistic individuality and a respect for portraits as works of art, the old workshop system had virtually disappeared. It is symptomatic of a changing ethos that the biographers of Victorian artists rarely talk about studio method.

The sitter's chair was normally placed on a dais so that it was on a level with the easel; Raeburn liked to position his sitters 'on a high platform, shortening the features ... The notion is that people should be painted as if they were hanging like pictures on the wall'.[40] Reynolds, always businesslike, bothered the normal run of his sitters as little as possible; he wrote to a client in 1777 that a portrait 'requires in general three sittings about an hour and half each time but if the sitter chooses it the face could be begun and finished in one day ... When the face is finished the rest is done without troubling the sitter.'[41] Lawrence is reported in 1804, when he had 'an overflow of new sitters', as operating in much the same way: 'He paints a Head at 3 sittings & is abt. 2 hours each time';[42] but he had five sittings

Fig. 13
Sir Joshua Reynolds: *Commodore Augustus Keppel* (*later Viscount Keppel*)
c. 1753–1754
Oil on canvas, 238.8 × 147 (94 × 58)
National Maritime Museum, Greenwich

from the Prince Regent for a portrait in robes for Oxford University, four for the head and one for the hand.[43] Lawrence's accommodating manners were noted at his sessions with the Allied leaders at Aix-la-Chapelle in 1819, when 'If the Empress of Austria made a remark upon a picture she found the next day that it had been attended to'.[44] Romney and Raeburn averaged four to six sittings. A century later John Lavery or Sargent might expect ten or twelve; Whistler, who would never be hurried, once imposed on a long-suffering sitter about sixty sittings of some four hours each.[45] There were by now no studio assistants to take the strain.

In the seventeenth century sitters were very often painted in clothes not their own, a practice which did not apply only to the allegorical portraits then popular. Lely in particular frequently painted his men in Indian gowns or silk vests and his women in night-gowns or shifts which could be arranged in elegant folds inviting a rich and lively manipulation of paint (Fig. 14). Gerard de Lairesse, in his *The Art of Painting*, 1738, recommends painters '*mixing the Fashion with what is Painter-like*; as the great *Lely* did'.[46] Reynolds, concerned that his portraits should not date, followed this precept; he also idealized many of his female sitters by the use of wrapping gowns or nondescript drapery which simulated classical sculpture – the portraitist, he advised, 'dresses his figure something with the general air of the antique for the sake of dignity, and preserves something of the modern for the sake of likeness' (Fig. 15).[47] Masquerade costume or Van Dyck dress were also popular in an age which enjoyed dressing-up (Fig. 16). In the nineteenth century, historicism may have been rampant throughout the arts, but not in portraiture, at any rate until the late Victorian nostalgia for the world of Gainsborough and Romney. From the time of Lawrence onwards sitters normally expected to be portrayed in their own clothes; Hoppner had a circular platform for a lay figure upon which he could arrange clothes borrowed from the sitter which it was an assistant's job to return. In their female portraits the Victorians compensated for their obsession with the factual everyday world by their delight

Fig. 14
Sir Peter Lely: *Anne Hyde, Duchess of York*
c. 1660
Oil on canvas, 182.2 × 143.8 ($71\frac{3}{4} × 56\frac{5}{8}$)
Scottish National Portrait Gallery, Edinburgh

Fig. 15
Sir Joshua Reynolds:
Lady Sarah Bunbury Sacrificing to the Graces
c. 1765
Oil on canvas, 242 × 151.5 ($95\frac{1}{4} × 59\frac{1}{2}$)
The Art Institute of Chicago,
Mr and Mrs W. W. Kimball Collection

Fig. 16
Thomas Gainsborough: *The Hon. Frances Duncombe*
c. 1778
Oil on canvas, 234.3 × 155.2 ($92\frac{1}{4} × 61\frac{1}{8}$)
The Frick Collection, New York

14

15

16

in high fashion and bright colour; but in their male portraits they were defeated by the trouser, which succeeded the more paintable breeches and pantaloons of earlier times, and by the collar and tie, items of dress which proved especially obdurate in sculpture.

The age of Lawrence was the last in which the majority of leading painters became portraitists as a matter of course, and for the most part painted little else. In the Victorian period the predominant genre was landscape. But, in spite of the prestige associated with successful subject pictures, and the large sums which were paid both for these and for landscapes, portraiture remained the most reliable means of earning a livelihood. John Millais turned to portraiture from Pre-Raphaelitism; Herkomer, Frank Holl and Fildes from social realism. The Society of Portrait Painters was founded in 1891, and the Edwardian era saw the apogee of society portraiture. Both Millais and Sir William Orpen were seduced by it. In the 1920s Orpen made an immense fortune from his practice (Fig. 17). Portraiture is inescapably a business arrangement for both artist and sitter – producer and purchaser – and Marcia Pointon is right to stress, in relation to the 1780s, though it is true also of other periods, that the works 'mulled over by admiring and discerning art historians were produced often in haste in a crowded studio by a portrait painter and his helpers who shunted the work off as quickly as possible to the various satellite industries of framing and engraving, varnishing and lining'.[48] But to a greater or lesser degree those works nonetheless all represent artistic ideals, and reflect the changing attitudes of society; and it is these aspects of British portraiture which need now to be examined.

Fig. 17
Sir William Orpen: *Sir Weetman Pearson, 2nd Viscount Cowdray*
Oil on canvas, 203.2 × 106.7 (80 × 42)
In the collection of the Viscount Cowdray

Holbein was one of the most penetrating portraitists who has ever lived, and his paintings and drawings of the courtiers and merchants of Henry VIII's London are unequalled in the history of British portraiture as a revelation of individual character and temperament (Fig. 18). 'With his unsurpassed control of line', Lorne Campbell has recently written, 'he had a capacity that has never been equalled to record, in a slightly exaggerated form and with superb economy, those imperfections in symmetry that distinguished his sitters.'[49] Associational details were often included to tabulate the interests and place in society of the personalities whose features Holbein so subtly described, but the vitality of the head was never diminished by the clothes or an exquisitely painted still-life.

Though no one was capable of the sensitivity with which Holbein worked, the influence of his style was paramount on the next generation of painters working in England: William Scrots (his successor as King's Painter), John Bettes, Master John, Gerlach Flicke and Hans Eworth. In later decades successive Netherlandish immigrants infused Flemish style into English portraiture, but they were caught up in the brashness and love of finery of an adventurous society. Magnificent costume and jewellery is the hallmark of Elizabethan painting, which was bright in colour and elaborate in pattern, iconic and (until the 1590s) two-dimensional, often symbolic in intent. The most exquisite and subtle painter of the age was the miniaturist, Hilliard, whose work Sir Ellis Waterhouse aptly described as 'most nearly paralleled by some of the finest of Persian miniatures', but with the added virtue of 'a prodigious gift of psychology' (Fig. 19).[50] The English School has been remarkably strong in miniature painting; Samuel Cooper (Fig. 20), by far the finest native painter of the Stuart period, was also a miniaturist with great insight into character.

In the later Jacobean period, and up to the arrival of Van Dyck in London in 1632, a more prosaic Dutch style prevailed in English painting, represented on the one hand by the solid full-lengths of Mytens and on the other by the gentle likenesses of Cornelius Johnson. Van Dyck brought an entirely new level of artistic quality into British portraiture (Fig. 21), and his sophistication, style, and range of compositions and poses had a profound influence on successive generations of portrait painters for almost 300 years. Gainsborough made large-scale copies of several of his portraits out of sheer delight, and the elegance of his own mature style is unimaginable without the intervention of Van Dyck. A hundred years later Fildes, on a visit to Genoa in 1887, described Van Dyck as 'a necessity for a portrait-painter's education'.[51] His style permeated the Edwardian grand manner, and the great master of that epoch, Sargent, was hailed by Rodin as 'the Van Dyck of our times'.[52]

As in the case of Holbein before him, and Kneller, Reynolds and Lawrence after him, it was inevitable that Van Dyck should exert a pervasive influence on the next generation of painters, those who practised portraiture during the Civil War and the fourteen years of the Commonwealth. William Dobson, painter of the wartime court at Oxford, with his bluff characterizations and coarse-textured paint (no. 6), was the exception. Lely seems to have come to England from Haarlem within a year or two of Van Dyck's demise. In the 1650s and 1660s a painter of often supreme accomplishment, he took up the family groups (no. 10), mythological guise and arcadianism of Van Dyck (Fig. 22), and imitated his patterns, poses and gestures; but his colour was generally richer, his chiaroscuro bolder, and his types,

Fig. 18
Hans Holbein: *George Gisze*
1532
Oil on panel, 96.3 × 85.7 (38 × 33¾)
Gemäldegalerie, Berlin

Fig. 19
Nicholas Hilliard: *Young Man Among Roses*,
probably Robert Devereux, 2nd Earl of Essex
c. 1587
Vellum on card; oval, 13.6 × 7.3 (5¼ × 2⅞)
The Trustees of
the Victoria & Albert Museum, London

Fig. 20
Samuel Cooper: *William Lenthall*
1652
Miniature on vellum; oval, 5.4 × 4.4 (2⅛ × 1¾)
National Portrait Gallery, London

Fig. 21
Sir Anthony van Dyck: *Lucy Percy, Countess of Carlisle*
c. 1637
Oil on canvas, 218.4 × 130.8 (86 × 51½)
The Trustees of the Rt. Hon. Olive,
Countess Fitzwilliam's Chattels Settlement,
and the Lady Juliet de Chair

whether tough-looking seadogs and politicians or the voluptuous and easy-going ladies of the Restoration court, more robust.

Kneller, who had first developed a style in the Rembrandtesque manner of Ferdinand Bol, came to England as a young man in 1674 or 1675, during Lely's last phase, when his technique was thinner and broader than hitherto. Kneller followed this tendency, and painted in a sober style, without any beauties of texture, employing a generally sombre palette; but he had at his disposition a wider range of compositions and poses than Lely, and was capable, on occasion, of an extraordinary immediacy (Fig. 23). From the accession of William III onwards his principal rival was the Swedish immigrant, Michael Dahl, who painted in a similar but gentler style, and outlived him by twenty years. John Closterman, from Osnabrück, could be more grandly baroque both in composition and the handling of drapery; and, after his visit to Rome in 1699, under the patronage of the distinguished moral philosopher, Lord Shaftesbury – an influential arbiter of taste of austere and classical leanings – he produced a number of earnest, classicizing portraits which anticipate the Neo-classicism of the 1760s.

The succession lay in the hands of Jonathan Richardson (no. 13), the pupil of John Riley – a diffident painter at his best with middle-class, even humble, sitters, who had died in 1691 – and of Charles Jervas, who spent six years in Rome, and was instantly acclaimed after his return to London in 1709. But Richardson was uninspired, and Jervas's pictures, even more than Lely's, were all 'brothers and sisters'; the future lay in a different direction, with a ravishing new continental style replacing the rhetoric of the Baroque, a style characterized by informality, intimacy and playfulness, curvilinear rhythms, sparkling surface pattern and gaiety of colour, namely the

Fig. 22
Sir Peter Lely: *Portrait of a Boy*
c. 1658–1660
Oil on canvas, 91.4 × 75.9 (36 × 29⅞)
The Governors of Dulwich Picture Gallery, London

Fig. 23
Sir Godfrey Kneller: *Matthew Prior*
1700
Oil on canvas, 137.8 × 102 (54¼ × 40⅛)
The Master and Fellows of Trinity College, Cambridge

Rococo. The principal exponent of rococo painting in England was that great artistic entrepreneur, Hogarth (no. 14), and it was he who, after it had been introduced in the mid-1720s by Philippe Mercier, developed its principal art form in this country – an informal and diminutive genre known as the conversation piece (see p. 66). Gainsborough's early portraits in landscapes, with their exquisite handling of paint (no. 21), and Tuscher's brightly coloured and lusciously painted portraits, animated by quivering drapery folds (no. 20), are excellent examples of the rococo spirit. Hudson, Ramsay and especially Cotes – who worked also in the typically rococo medium of pastel – all exploited for painterly effect the silks, laces and satins, bows, ruching and flounces, of the exceptionally lovely contemporary fashions (Fig. 24).

For Reynolds, steeped in the theories of Shaftesbury and Richardson and well-versed in the art of classical antiquity, the Rococo was anathema: 'all trifling or artful play of little lights, or an attention to a variety of tints is to be avoided . . . It is the inferior stile that marks the variety of stuffs'.[53] What he called 'the great stile' depended upon universals not particulars, and Reynolds sought to raise the art of portraiture in the academic hierarchy by idealizing his sitters, generalizing his effects, and borrowing attitudes from classical sculpture and Renaissance or seventeenth-century history painting. Many of his male sitters were exalted as exemplars of aristocratic standing or of their profession or calling (no. 29); some of his female sitters were transformed into goddesses, or occasionally saints, sustained by a more thoroughgoing invention than those of Lely or Kneller, or became embodiments of domesticity or of moods such as contemplation or pastoral reverie; children were treated as innocents. Reynolds commanded an immense range of designs and poses, and, both through his position as President of the Academy and the succession of major works he contributed annually to its exhibitions, he exerted a great influence on his contemporaries, not all of whom, however, were as serious in their approach as he. Romney, his principal rival, had a more superficial mind, both in respect of literature and visual imagery, but, as Desmond Shawe-Taylor has argued, he invested his female sitters with the prevailing feminine virtues of simplicity, modesty, faithfulness and domesticity (Fig. 25), sometimes, like Wright of Derby, through the medium of literary characters drawn from uplifting poems or tracts or from popular romances.[54] In this he was at the heart of the late eighteenth-century cult of *sensibilité*, which deeply affected Gainsborough and which that artist expressed through his 'cottage door' landscapes and his much acclaimed fancy pictures of beggar children, works done in the last decade of his life.

Gainsborough did not follow 'the great stile' and derived his aesthetic from the Rococo, from the sharply observed naturalism of Hogarth and Roubiliac. He regarded likeness, not idealization, as 'the principal beauty & intention of a Portrait'[55] and hated the very thought of 'a handsom Face [being] overset by a fictitious bundle of trumpery of the foolish Painters own inventing'.[56] He had only the most rudimentary studio organization and preferred to paint entirely from the life; indeed his friend Philip Thicknesse remarked of his portraits that they could be judged as though they were the living persons. Gainsborough, like Holbein, was concerned to catch individual expressions, gestures and movements, though he achieved this with an impressionistic touch rather than by line. Reynolds acknowledged that 'he neglected nothing which could keep his

Fig. 24
Francis Cotes: *Princess Louisa and her sister, Queen Caroline Matilda of Denmark*
1767
Oil on canvas, 265.7 × 186.7 (104⅝ × 73½)
Royal Collection, Buckingham Palace, London (by gracious permission of Her Majesty The Queen)

faculties in exercise ... he had a habit of continually remarking to those who happened to be about him, whatever peculiarity of countenance, whatever accidental combination of figures, or happy effects of light and shadow, occurred in prospects, in the sky, in walking the streets, or in company.'[57] Gainsborough's particular contribution to the evolution of British portraiture was a feeling for movement most apparent in his late works. Whereas Reynolds, even in his liveliest late designs, always retained his concern for the figure as a concept and respected the limits of the picture frame, Gainsborough enveloped a living and breathing presence within magnificent trees that are part of a broader landscape, often showing his sitter poised as though in converse (Fig. 16) or beginning to walk out of the canvas (no. 41).

The young Lawrence took up from where Gainsborough had left off. In his portrait of the actress, Elizabeth Farren (one of the two full-lengths exhibited in 1790 which established his reputation) (Fig. 26), he brought the spectator into the closest possible touch with his sitter by employing a low viewpoint, so that she seems to move across the scene right in front of our eyes, her charming face turned gaily towards us framed by fast-moving clouds. Lawrence consistently used low viewpoints as well as freshness of colour and a dazzling *facture* to give presence and vitality to his sitters; and his wonderfully expressive style, synonomous with the romantic portrait, inaugurated an era in which almost every proficient portraitist, not just an exceptional master like Van Dyck or Gainsborough, was accepted as an artist rather than as a superior craftsman running a business, as Hudson had been content to be, and Reynolds, for all his airs, in some respects remained. Abroad, David and Goya were the catalysts.

Lawrence's successors were workmanlike and sometimes not unaccomplished portraitists; they included contemporaries of his like Thomas Phillips and Shee who worked on into the 1840s, John Partridge and Sir George Hayter, Frederick Say, Stephen Pearce and Henry Pickersgill, who last exhibited at the Academy in 1872. But,

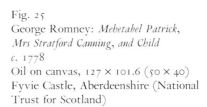

Fig. 25
George Romney: *Mehetabel Patrick, Mrs Stratford Canning, and Child*
c. 1778
Oil on canvas, 127 × 101.6 (50 × 40)
Fyvie Castle, Aberdeenshire (National Trust for Scotland)

Fig. 26
Sir Thomas Lawrence: *Elizabeth Farren (later Countess of Derby)*
1790
Oil on canvas, 238.8 × 146.1 (94 × 57½)
Metropolitan Museum of Art, New York

Fig. 27
Sir Francis Grant: *Colonel George Wyndham*
Oil on canvas, 236.2 × 144.8 (93 × 57)
The Lord Egremont, Petworth House, Sussex

25

26

27

after the death of Wilkie, only two were in any way remarkable: Winterhalter, Queen Victoria's favourite portrait painter, a superb painter of costume, who was based in Paris and admirably reflected the somewhat febrile glitter of the Second Empire; and Sir Francis Grant, who specialized in portraits of the hunting aristocracy and their horses and handled paint with something of the elegance and assurance of Lawrence (Fig. 27).

Watts, sometimes profound (see p. 136) but often turgid in actual handling, began his gallery of heads of great contemporaries in the 1850s. Watts apart, the most brilliant, original and penetrating portraitists at mid-century were the Pre-Raphaelites, who, however, chiefly painted and drew themselves or their friends (see p. 138 and Fig. 28). Burne-Jones, a second generation Pre-Raphaelite, best known for his mythologies and medievalizing, also executed a number of portraits, some on commission, which were haunting, subtly monochrome, and beautifully designed or patterned (Fig. 29). But arguably the greatest portraitist working in England in the second half of the nineteenth century was another exquisite artist, the American, James McNeill Whistler. Whistler was principally concerned with pictorial values, and most of his full-length portraits were entitled 'Arrangement' or 'Harmony'. In his later works, indeed, he became increasingly shadowy, though, as he wrote, if 'the buttons are lost ... the sitter remains.'[58] And Whistler, who combined aestheticism with an intuitive understanding of his fellow men and women, especially women, had an unerring eye for the expression and posture of his sitters that was most deeply revealing

Fig. 28
William Bell Scott: *Algernon Charles Swinburne*
c. 1860
Oil on canvas, 46.4 × 31.8 (18¼ × 12½)
The Master and Fellows of Balliol College, Oxford

Fig. 29
Sir Edward Burne-Jones: *The Countess of Plymouth*
1893
Oil on canvas, 199.4 × 94 (78½ × 37)
The Viscount Windsor, Oakly Park, Shropshire

Fig. 30
James McNeill Whistler:
Symphony in Flesh Colour and Pink: Portrait of Mrs Frances Leyland
1871–1874
Oil on canvas, 195.9 × 102.2 (77 × 40¼)
The Frick Collection, New York

28

30

of their character: with the exception of his early, revolutionary profiles of his mother and Carlyle, no two of his poses are more than superficially the same. Unfortunately, Whistler was very demanding. Mrs Leyland, wife of the shipping magnate, had wanted to be painted in black velvet, but the artist decreed otherwise (Fig. 30); moreover, he was a perfectionist who required innumerable sittings – without seeming to his victim to achieve much thereby. Perhaps, above all, in an age when people, often newly wealthy, were unusually conscious of the importance of their standing in society, he was producing the wrong kind of portrait. In any event, he never succeeded in his ambition to paint 'all the fashionables'.[59]

The requisite realistic public likeness was supplied by a number of artists, headed by Millais, who took to portraiture when demand accelerated in the latter part of the Victorian age; principal among these were Holl (Fig. 31), Fildes and Herkomer, together with William Ouless and Frank Dicksee, who were still painting in the 1920s when the field was held by Orpen and Augustus John. It was Sargent, however, a designer of astonishing brilliance who excelled in group portraits and a painter endowed with a miraculous touch, who expressed to the full, through the sheer virtuosity of his flowing brushwork, the boundless self-confidence of the late Victorian and Edwardian upper classes (Fig. 32).

Sargent inevitably had followers who sought to emulate his success, but it was Whistler to whom young artists, such as William Rothenstein and William Nicholson, instinctively turned. It was not only his style and his designs and his sense of pattern (Fig. 33) but his

Fig. 31
Frank Holl: *Sir William S. Gilbert*
1886
Oil on canvas, 100.3 × 125.7 (39½ × 49½)
National Portrait Gallery, London

Fig. 32
John Singer Sargent: *Sir Frank Swettenham*
1904
Oil on canvas, 170.8 × 110.5 (67¼ × 43½)
National Portrait Gallery, London

independence of outlook that captured their allegiance. Walter Sickert, who worked in Whistler's studio and learnt a great deal from the master, later found his true mentor in Degas, just as Harold Gilman and Spencer Gore, who congregated round Sickert in Fitzroy Street in the mid-1900s, were to reject that artist's low-keyed palette in favour of the thick paint and bright colours of Post-Impressionism for their own realistic middle-class subjects (Fig. 34). Ambrose McEvoy, who was encouraged by Whistler and painted with Sickert in Dieppe, was not alone in developing a markedly personal style when, from about 1915, he began to pursue a career as a society portraitist. Glyn Philpot could be startlingly modern in his painting of the 1930s (Fig. 35). Artists who painted powerful portraits but were not primarily portraitists included John Duncan Fergusson and his Scottish associates, who were attracted by the Fauves; Wyndham Lewis and William Roberts, who responded to Futurism; Mark Gertler, Bernard Meninsky and Stanley Spencer. In the aftermath of Whistler style became as varied as the exhibiting societies which proliferated in antagonism to the Academy, a process which was to continue with approaches to the art as contrasted as those of Sir William Coldstream and Graham Sutherland and with the work of the most significant artists practising portraiture today.

Fig. 33
Sidney Starr: *Gertrude Kingston*
1888
Oil on canvas, 108.3 × 82.8 (42⅝ × 32⅝)
Ferens Art Gallery, Hull

Fig. 34
Harold Gilman: *Mrs Mounter at the Breakfast Table*
1916
Oil on canvas, 61 × 40.6 (24 × 16)
Tate Gallery, London

Fig. 35
Glyn Philpot: *M. Julien Zaire (Tom Whiskey)*
1931–1932
Oil on canvas, 44 × 31.8 (17½ × 12½)
Private Collection

Notes

1. The sub-title of Roy Strong, *Henry, Prince of Wales*, 1986.

2. James Northcote, *The Life of Sir Joshua Reynolds*, 2nd edn, 2 vols, 1819, vol. 1, p. 54.

3. *Vertue Note Books*, vol. 3, Walpole Society, vol. 22, 1934, p. 79.

4. See Ellis Kirkham Waterhouse, *Three Decades of British Art 1740–1770*, Philadelphia, 1965, pp. 65–8.

5. *The Diary of Joseph Farington*, 24 February 1803 (ed. Kenneth Garlick and Angus Macintyre, 16 vols, New Haven and London, vol. 5, 1979, p. 1986).

6. Gainsborough to David Garrick (Bath, 1766) (Mary Woodall, ed., *The Letters of Thomas Gainsborough*, 2nd edn revised, Cupid Press, 1963, no. 26, p. 63).

7. Gainsborough to William Johnstone Pulteney, Bath, n.d. (Woodall, op. cit., no. 66, p. 127).

8. Anon. (= Thomas Green), 'The Diary of a Lover of Literature', *The Gentleman's Magazine*, March 1834, p. 252.

9. *The Diary of Joseph Farington*, 23 and 26 April 1799 (ed. Garlick and Macintyre, op. cit., vol. 4, 1979, pp. 1208–9 and 1212).

10. Sir George Clausen, 'Autobiographical Notes' (quoted in Kenneth McConkey, *Edwardian Portraits: Images of an Age of Opulence*, Woodbridge, 1987, p. 26).

11. Reynolds to Charles, 4th Duke of Rutland, London, 24 September 1784 (Frederick Whiley Hilles, ed., *Letters of Sir Joshua Reynolds*, Cambridge, Mass., 1929, no. 76, p. 112).

12. L. V. Fildes, *Luke Fildes, R.A.: A Victorian Painter*, 1968, pp.159–60.

13. Quentin Bell, *Bad Art*, London, 1989, p. 95.

14. McConkey, op. cit., p. 52.

15. André Rouquet, *The Present State of the Arts in England*, 1755, p. 45.

16. Hubert von Herkomer, *Five Lectures delivered to the Students of the Royal Academy, January 1900*, privately printed, 1900, p. 29 (quoted in David Setford, 'Herkomer – A Passion for Work', *A Passion for Work – Sir Hubert von Herkomer 1849–1914*, Watford Museum, 1982, p. 8).

17. London, 27 July 1676 (published in William James Smith, 'Letters from Michael Wright', *The Burlington Magazine*, vol. 95, July 1953, p. 234).

18. *The Diary of Joseph Farington*, 17 February 1809 (ed. Kathryn Cave, op. cit., vol. 9, 1982, p. 3401).

19. Marcia Pointon, 'Portrait-Painting as a Business Enterprise in London in the 1780s', *Art History*, vol. 7, no. 2, June 1984, p. 190.

20. *The Diary of Joseph Farington*, 6 January 1799 (ed. Garlick and Macintyre, op. cit., vol. 4, 1979, p. 1130).

21. Northcote, op. cit., vol. 2, p. 25.

22. Philip Thicknesse, *A Sketch of the Life and Paintings of Thomas Gainsborough, Esq.*, 1788, p. 8.

23. Margaret Whinney and Oliver Millar, *English Art 1625–1714*, Oxford, 1957, pp. 81 and 83.

24. *Vertue Note Books*, vol. 3, Walpole Society, vol. 22, 1934, p. 111.

25. Gainsborough to William Mayhew, Ipswich, 24 February 1757 and 13 March 1758 (Woodall, op. cit., no. 24, p. 61, and no. 25, p. 61).

26. T. Clayton, ed., *The Works of Sir John Suckling*, London, 1971, p. 121 (quoted in Sir Oliver Millar, *Van Dyck in England*, exh. cat., National Portrait Gallery, 1982, p. 30; Millar discusses Van Dyck's methods of work in his later years, pp. 29–31).

27. *The Diary of Samuel Pepys*, 25 March 1667 (ed. Robert Latham and William Matthews, 11 vols, 1970–1983, vol. 8, 1974, p. 129.)

28. *The Diary of Samuel Pepys*, 20 October 1662 (ibid., vol. 3, 1970, p. 230).

29. Wright to Sir Walter Bagot, London, 27 July 1676 (Smith, op. cit., p. 234).

30. *The Diary of Samuel Pepys*, 18 April 1666 (ed. Latham and Matthews, op. cit., vol. 7, 1972, p. 102).

31. Sir Oliver Millar, *Sir Peter Lely 1618–80*, exh. cat., National Portrait Gallery, 1978, p. 17.

32. Anon., British Library Add.MS.22950, f.41 (quoted in Whinney and Millar, op. cit., p. 174).

33. Wright to Sir Walter Bagot, London, 27 July 1676 (Smith, op. cit., p. 234).

34. Whinney and Millar, op. cit., p. 195.

35. *Vertue Note Books*, vol. 3, Walpole Society, vol. 22, 1934, p. 151.

36. Ellen Miles, *Thomas Hudson 1701–1779*, exh. cat., Iveagh Bequest, Kenwood, 1979, introduction, p. 1 (cat. unpaginated).

37. Lawrence to Edmund Antrobus (Coutts & Co. Archives) (quoted in Kenneth Garlick, *Sir Thomas Lawrence*, Oxford, 1989, p. 14).

38. *The Diary of Joseph Farington*, 16 December 1803 (ed. Garlick and Macintyre, op. cit., vol. 6, 1979, p. 2193).

39. Northcote, op. cit., vol. 1, p. 102.

40. Dr John Brown, one of Raeburn's sitters (quoted by James Greig, *Sir Henry Raeburn, R.A.*, 1911, p. xxxvii).

41. Reynolds to Daniel Daulby, London, 9 September 1777 (Hilles, op. cit., no. 40, p. 56).

42. *The Diary of Joseph Farington*, 30 May 1804 (ed. Garlick and Macintyre, op. cit., vol. 6, 1979, p. 2334).

43. Ibid., 23 March 1818 (ed. Cave, op. cit., vol. 15, 1984, p. 5179).

44. Ibid., 11 December 1819 (ed. Cave, op. cit., vol. 15, 1984, p. 5437).

45. McConkey, op. cit., p. 25.

46. Quoted in Desmond Shawe-Taylor, *The Georgians: Eighteenth-Century Portraiture & Society*, 1990, p. 149.

47. *Discourse Seven*, 10 December 1776 (ed. Robert R. Wark, *Sir Joshua Reynolds: Discourses on Art*, 2nd edn, New Haven, 1975, p. 140).

48. Pointon, op. cit., p. 201.

49. Lorne Campbell, *Renaissance Portraits*, New Haven and London, 1990, p. 12.

50. Ellis Waterhouse, *Painting in Britain 1530 to 1790*, Harmondsworth, 1953, p. 23.

51. Fildes, op. cit., p. 109.

52. Quoted in McConkey, op. cit., p. 27.

53. *Discourse Four*, 10 December 1771 (ed. Wark, op. cit., pp. 61–2).

54. Shawe-Taylor, op. cit., pp. 120–2.

55. Gainsborough to William, 2nd Earl of Dartmouth, Bath, 13 April 1771 (ed. Woodall, op. cit., no. 17, p. 51).

56. Gainsborough to William, 2nd Earl of Dartmouth, Bath, 18 April (1771) (ed. Woodall, op. cit., no. 18, p. 53).

57. *Discourse Fourteen*, 10 December 1788 (ed. Wark, op. cit., p. 250).

58. Quoted in Denys Sutton, *James McNeill Whistler*, 1966, p. 41.

59. Quoted in ibid., p. 38.

Catalogue Note

The entries go beyond descriptions and analysis of the individual works and have been written as far as the evidence permits to set the portraits within the context of the sitter's life, the artist's career and the development of British portraiture. Provenance has been given in full, but the literature section has been confined to the principal and most illuminating references; since many of the most important discussions, especially in recent years, are contained in exhibition catalogues, these have been included in the literature section, with the author's name cited; the relevant NACF Report has been cited in each instance. Exhibition references without significant text matter are almost entirely restricted to the original exhibition of the works in question, and are normally cited in the context of the portrait's date. References to the illustration of the works in books or catalogues have been excluded. Complete references appropriate to a catalogue raisonné are usually contained within one or other of the publications mentioned. The place of publication, or location of an exhibition, has been omitted where it is London. Sizes have been given in centimetres, with inches in parentheses, height before width.

I

An Unknown Lady

Marcus Gheeraerts the Younger (active by 1561 – died 1635)

Oil on canvas, 204.5 × 117.5 (80½ × 46¼)
Inscribed above the chair t.r.: *1618*

Ferens Art Gallery: Hull City Museums and Art Galleries (548)

George Gower: *Mary Cornwallis*
1580–1585 (?)
Oil on panel, 117.2 × 94 (46⅛ × 37)
Manchester City Art Gallery

The sitter in this portrait has not been identified. An inscription added at a later date wrongly identifies her as the Infanta Isabella Clara Eugenia; she was subsequently also misidentified as Frances Howard, Countess of Essex and Somerset. With the growing archival resources provided by the National Portrait Gallery, serious iconographical study has tempered the enthusiasm of earlier owners of important Elizabethan portraits to give their pictures high-sounding identities.

Continued research over the last seventy-five years or so has established an œuvre for Marcus Gheeraerts the Younger, subsequent to his early career in the Low Countries, which, as Sir Roy Strong observed, is 'the most extensive yet uncovered of an Elizabethan painter'. From about 1590 he was patronized by Queen Elizabeth's pageant-master, Sir Henry Lee, for whom he painted the famous portrait of the queen (National Portrait Gallery), probably to commemorate her visit to Ditchley in 1592. Gheeraerts, inventive and in his exoticism in tune with the times, was the leading portraitist in England by the turn of the century, and became Anne of Denmark's chosen painter. Although he was paid for four royal full-length portraits as late as 1618, he was, however, already being superseded at court by this time by fresh painters from the Low Countries: Paul van Somer and Abraham van Blyenberch, and, most importantly, Daniel Mytens. His style remained unaffected, but his commissions now came chiefly from the lesser gentry and from academic circles. In temper and in the soft modelling of his heads his later work was closely akin to that of Cornelius Johnson.

The essence of Elizabethan painting had been its concentration on pattern – on the careful rendition of the colourful costume and jewellery of the period (see comparative illustration). Gheeraerts's contribution to the Elizabethan costume piece, exemplified in this full-length portrait of 1618, was to set it more firmly within the realistic Flemish tradition through his ability to set his sitters convincingly in space, and his capacity for modelling the heads in his portraits with greater solidity and more vivid naturalism. The pronounced tubular folds of the dress in this portrait, characteristic of contemporary fashion, help to give the figure a greater sense of volume. The sobriety of colour is characteristic of Jacobean, as opposed to Elizabethan, costume. The motif of the sitter fingering the pearls at her waist probably refers to the womb and to expected childbirth.

Gheeraerts repeated the pose and pattern of this work, with variations, for his full-length portrait of Lady Russell, painted in 1625 (Woburn Abbey). The formula is close to that used by William Larkin in many of his portraits of the 1610s.

Provenance: The Dukes of Marlborough by 1816; Duke of Marlborough (Blenheim Palace) sale, Christie's, 31 July, 3 and 4 August 1886, 2nd day, lot 240 (as Frances Howard, Countess of Essex and Somerset), bt. Colnaghi's; C. Butler; by descent to his grandson C.H.A. Butler; Butler sale, Christie's, 8 May 1964, lot 59 (still as above), bt. Agnew's, from whom it was purchased, 1965.

Literature: NACF Report, 1965, p. 20; Roy Strong, *The English Icon: Elizabethan & Jacobean Portraiture*, 1969, p. 294.

Henry, Prince of Wales

Robert Peake the Elder (active by 1576 – 1626?)

Oil on canvas, 172.8 × 113.7 (68 × 44¾)
c.1611–1612

National Portrait Gallery, London (4515)

Henry Frederick (1594–1612), the eldest son of James I and Anne of Denmark, was created Prince of Wales in 1610. The prince was determined to bring international distinction and modernity to his new court at St James's Palace, and, as Sir Roy Strong has recently stressed, it was largely under the tutelage of the Florentine polymath, Constantino de' Servi, whom the Grand Duke of Tuscany released for service in London, that the handsome young heir to the throne grew up a true Renaissance prince, as learned and cultivated in literature and the arts as he was energetic and manly in feats of arms and sports of all kinds. His particular interest lay in garden planning, and first his architect, Salomon de Caus, then de' Servi, carried out extensive works at the prince's palace at Richmond, much on the model of the Villa d'Este at Tivoli. Inigo Jones was the prince's Surveyor. Tragically Prince Henry died of typhoid fever at the age of eighteen, and with him died his renaissance of the arts in England; he was succeeded as heir apparent by his equally cultivated but less charismatic brother, Charles. Henry and his sister, Elizabeth (the 'Winter Queen'), the first owner of this portrait (see no. 9), were devoted to each other.

Robert Peake, a leading portraitist of the 1590s influenced by Nicholas Hilliard, lacked the sound draughtsmanship and the stature of Marcus Gheeraerts, but nonetheless was appointed Principal Painter to the youthful Prince Henry on the accession of James I in 1603. Peake's first portrait of his new patron was the large and ambitious canvas (see comparative illustration) showing him out hunting with his closest friend, John Harington, whose father was responsible for his sister Elizabeth's education. The Gallery's portrait is more traditional and, consequently, more colourful and richly patterned. Henry is seen wearing the insignia of the Order of the Garter with, beside him, a plumed hat bearing a jewel in the form of the letters HP (Henricus Princeps). The distant view has not been (and could not be) identified, but the glimpse of lake, gardens and eyot almost certainly represents, or at least symbolizes, the project closest to the prince's heart, the great garden at Richmond. The confident stance and gaze belie Peake's deficiencies: the right arm is stiffly drawn and is unrelated to the table on which it is resting. By this date Prince Henry was looking beyond the archaic concepts and limited talents of Peake to artists with a more Continental perspective, such as Isaac Oliver, and tried to attract Michiel van Miereveld to London.

Provenance: Elizabeth, Queen of Bohemia (Henry's sister); either given by her to her devoted friend, William, 1st Earl of Craven, or bequeathed to him later by Prince Rupert, who inherited many of his mother's possessions; thence by descent to Cornelia, Countess of Craven; purchased by private treaty sale, with five other early seventeenth-century portraits, from the Craven Trustees, 1966.

Literature: NACF Report, 1966, p. 27; Roy Strong, *The English Icon: Elizabethan & Jacobean Portraiture*, 1969, p. 248.

Robert Peake the Elder: *Henry Frederick, Prince of Wales and Sir John Harington*
1612
Oil on canvas, 198.7 × 145 (79½ × 58)
The Metropolitan Museum of Art, New York,
Purchase 1944, Joseph Pulitzer Bequest

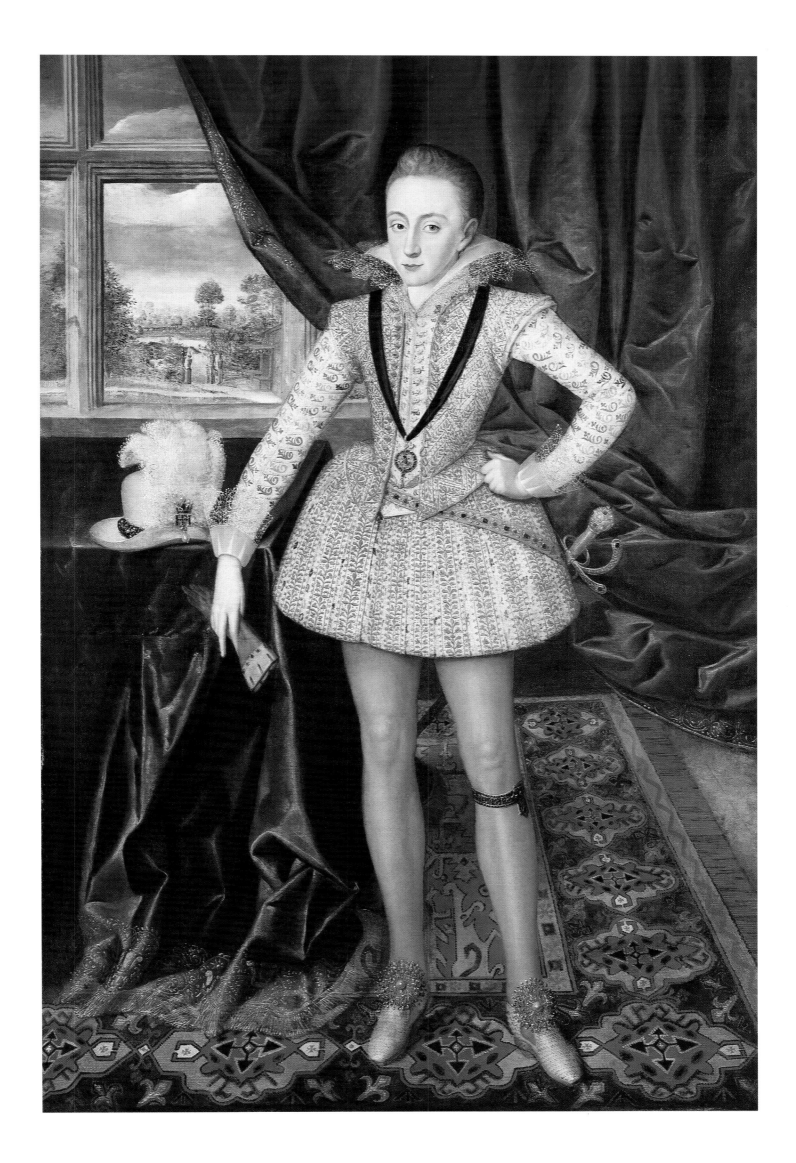

3

Charles I

Gerard van Honthorst (1590–1656)

Oil on canvas, 76.2 × 64.1 (30 × 25¼)
1628

National Portrait Gallery, London (4444)

Charles I (1600–1649) became king in 1625, succeeding his father, James I. As inflexibly opposed as James to the rise of Puritanism and the principle of religious toleration, his troubles stemmed from his determination to keep as his first minister his intimate friend George Villiers, Duke of Buckingham, whom successive Parliaments rightly distrusted and determined to remove (he was assassinated at Portsmouth in 1628). Incapable of negotiating with his opponents – able, serious and honest men who sought religious and constitutional liberty – Charles resorted first to unconstitutional expedients for raising the revenues begrudged by Parliament, then to eleven years of personal rule. The recall of Parliament in 1640 (to vote funds for the Scottish War, the Presbyterians, unaccountably to Charles, having revolted against the imposition of the Anglican Book of Common Prayer) led inexorably to political conflict, the Great Rebellion, five years of civil war, and, ultimately, the execution of the monarch. In private life, Charles was exemplary: virtuous, religious and exceptionally cultivated. As Sir Oliver Millar has written, he was 'the most enthusiastic and discerning patron of the arts to grace the English throne and he assembled a collection of pictures and works of art unequalled in the history of English taste'.

Honthorst, a pupil of Abraham Bloemart, travelled to Rome between 1610 and 1612 and, after his return to Utrecht in 1620, became the leading exponent with Baburen and Terbrugghen of the Caravaggesque style in Holland. He had been under scrutiny as a rising star by English connoisseurs since 1621 and preceded Rubens and Van Dyck to the Caroline court in 1628; the principal purpose of his six months' visit was the execution of the huge courtly allegory of *Apollo and Diana*, in which Buckingham appeared as Mercury presenting the Seven Liberal Arts to the king, for the Queen's Staircase at Hampton Court.

Honthorst's gentle portrait, which shows Charles in contemplative mood, as a withdrawn scholar rather than as the defender of Buckingham and upholder of the Divine Right of Kings (see comparative illustration), was an *ad vivum* study for his distinctly unromantic representation of the king as Apollo. Its breadth of handling reflects Honthorst's long experience of Italian style.

Provenance: Ulysse Moussalli, Paris; Moussalli sale, Sotheby's, 24 March 1965, lot 101A, bt. Leggatt on behalf of the National Portrait Gallery.

Literature: NACF Report, 1965, p. 22.

Sir Anthony van Dyck: *Charles I on horseback with M. de St Antoine*
1633
Oil on canvas, 368.4 × 269.9 (145 × 106¼)
Royal Collection, Buckingham Palace, London
(by gracious permission of Her Majesty The Queen)

4

James, 1st Duke of Hamilton

Daniel Mytens (c.1590–1647)

Oil on canvas, 203.6 × 139.9 (80 × 55)
1629

Scottish National Portrait Gallery (PG 2722)

James, 1st Duke of Hamilton (1606–1649), was a close friend of
Charles I and played a leading role in the formation of the king's
great art collection. He also formed a fine collection of his own,
partly acquired in Venice. Because he was a great landowner with
enormous hereditary influence in Scotland, Charles appointed him
commissioner in 1638 to pacify the country after the attempted
introduction of the new prayer book had resulted in the signature
of the national covenant. But Hamilton was no Strafford, no man
of action; he possessed little strength of purpose, was given to
intrigue and compromise, and was concerned principally to
safeguard his own estates. During the ten years he spent at the
centre of the complex web of Scottish affairs he betrayed everyone
in turn; he had displayed singular military ineptitude when
commanding the British forces supporting the Protestant cause in
Germany, 1630–1634, and the end of his career came typically
when he led a huge Scottish army into England in 1648, failed to
deploy it in battle, and was coolly routed by Cromwell. He
surrendered, and was tried and executed.

Daniel Mytens, who had entered the Guild of St Luke in
The Hague in 1610, came to England in or before 1618, and in
the summer of that year was working for the Earl of Arundel. In
1624 he entered the royal service with a stipend of fifty pounds a
year. His bold, realistic Dutch style, with its restrained use of
colour, made a dramatic contrast with the rich and colourful
pattern-making of Gheeraerts and Peake, and the confident
elegance of the full-lengths he painted before his return to The
Hague (certainly by 1635) prefigured the cosmopolitan swagger
of Van Dyck, who settled in London in 1632.

James Hamilton was eighteen when Mytens first painted him
full-length (Tate Gallery), and twenty-three when he painted this
portrait – Hamilton had just taken up residence in London,
having been made a Privy Councillor and Master of the Horse in
succession to the assassinated Buckingham. The delicate and
unusual colour harmonies – the grey costume embroidered with
silver which catches the light, and the pale blue curtain behind,
free of the elaborate and obtrusive broken folds characteristic of
the Jacobean repertory of forms – betoken the glamorous young
courtier. But the steady gaze and firm pose as surely depict
Hamilton as he wanted to be seen, not the puffed-up would-be
military commander Van Dyck unerringly portrayed some ten
years later. Again, powerful and arresting though the portrait is –
and it is Mytens' masterpiece – it cannot compete with the
sophisticated poses, brilliant handling, and sheer vitality of Van
Dyck's works in the same vein. Compare for dynamic tension
even the similarly placed legs in the great Flemish master's
portrait of the Earl of Warwick (see comparative illustration).

Provenance: By descent from the sitter to Angus, 15th Duke of Hamilton,
from whom it was purchased, 1987.

Literature: Sir Oliver Millar in Margaret Whinney and Oliver Millar,
English Art 1625–1714, Oxford, 1957, pp. 63–4; Duncan Thomson,
'Two Hamilton Portraits', NACF Review, 1988, pp. 112–13.

Sir Anthony van Dyck: *Robert Rich, Earl of Warwick*
1634
Oil on canvas, 213.4 × 128 (84 × 50⅜)
The Metropolitan Museum of Art, New York,
The Jules Bache Collection

5

Lord George Stuart, the 9th Seigneur d'Aubigny

Sir Anthony van Dyck (1599–1641)

Oil on canvas, 218.4 × 133.4 (86 × 52½)
*c.*1638

National Portrait Gallery, London (5964)

Sir Anthony van Dyck: *Philip, 4th Baron Wharton*
1632
Oil on canvas, 133 × 106 (52¼ × 41¾)
National Gallery of Art, Washington D.C.
Wharton is inscribed as aged about nineteen.

Joseph Wright of Derby: *Sir Brooke Boothby*
1781
Oil on canvas, 148.6 × 207.6 (58½ × 81¾)
Tate Gallery, London
*Boothby is pointing with his gloved finger to the name of the author
'Rousseau' on the spine of his book. The picture is not an image of
melancholy or self-doubt, but of a newly awakening world of feeling.*

Lord George Stuart (1618–1642) was the third son of Esmé
Stuart, 3rd Duke of Lennox. The scion of a prominent Catholic
family, he succeeded at the age of fourteen to the seigneurie of
Aubigny in the Loire and was brought up in France. At the
outbreak of the Civil War he raised 300 cavalry with which he
joined the royal standard; he fell, covered with wounds, at the
Battle of Edgehill, 1642, leading the Duke of York's troop in the
Prince of Wales's regiment of horse. He was aged twenty-four.

Van Dyck, the most talented member of Rubens's workshop,
spent six years in Italy, chiefly in Genoa, and four in Antwerp,
before settling in the spring of 1632 in London (the city he had
visited briefly in 1620–1621 in order to work for James I and the
Earl of Arundel). He was a religious, historical and mythological
painter of great sensitivity as well as a portraitist, but found little
demand for such work at the court of Charles I. The sensuous
and poetic *Cupid and Psyche* (Kensington Palace) is his only
surviving mythological work from this period.

This full-length was painted at the time of Lord George's
secret marriage, in 1638, to Lady Katherine Howard, daughter of
the Earl of Suffolk; the match was strongly disapproved of both
by his wife's family, and by his guardian the king. In this picture,
as in an earlier portrait in the same vein, that of Sir John Suckling
(Frick Collection, New York), the complex meaning of which has
been brilliantly unravelled by Malcolm Rogers, the sitter leans on
a rocky ledge bearing a Latin inscription which sets the mood, in
this case: *ME FIRMIOR AMOR* (Love is stronger than I am). In
other words, he had no choice but to resist both monarch and
father-in-law. For her part Katherine was willing to be 'declared a
Papist'; 'love hath been the principal agent in her conversion', it
was reported. Van Dyck has portrayed the young cavalier in
fanciful Arcadian dress, holding a *houlette*, as if for a court masque;
beneath the inscription is a rosebush, and at his feet a thistle,
symbolic of the pleasures and pains of love. Towards the end of
his life, worn out by overwork, Van Dyck became increasingly
mannered; but this canvas is one of the most deeply sensitive and
harmonious of his late works, as poetic in its way as the *Cupid and
Psyche* painted contemporaneously. The head, exquisitely
modelled, is imbued with a profound melancholy; in keeping with
this mood, the colours are soft and subdued, the lighting tender.
Only the cape has a baroque flourish. Although evocative of a
pastoral reverie, the picture has an underlying sturdiness more
obviously characteristic of an earlier picture in the same vein,
that of the young Philip, Lord Wharton (see comparative
illustration), the composition of which Van Dyck adapted and
refined for the present work: George Stuart was as natural and
brave a warrior as he was steadfast in love. This quality sets it
apart from comparable painting associated with the late
eighteenth-century cult of *sensibilité* (see comparative illustration).

Provenance: Passed to the sister of the last Duke of Richmond and Lennox
(died 1672), and ultimately to her granddaughter, Theodosia, Baroness
Clifton, Countess of Darnley; thence by descent to Adam, 11th Earl of
Darnley, from whom it was bought by H. Shickman Gallery, New York,
1986; purchased after export deferral, 1987.

Literature: Sir Oliver Millar, *Van Dyck in England*, exh. cat., National Portrait
Gallery, 1982, no. 61; Malcolm Rogers, 'Two 17th-Century Portraits',
NACF Review, 1988, p. 79.

6

Colonel Richard Neville

William Dobson (1611–1646)

Oil on canvas, 114 × 91.4 (44⅞ × 36)
*c.*1643–1644

National Portrait Gallery, London (5382)

From at least as early as 1713, when a version was engraved for Ward's *History of the Rebellion*, this portrait was believed to represent Sir Charles Lucas, the dashing royalist cavalry commander, who was executed at Colchester in 1648. The sitter has now been identified as Richard Neville (1615–1676), of Billingbear, Berkshire (where the portrait was recorded in 1797). Neville was also a royalist cavalry commander in the Civil War, succeeding Lord Carnarvon in command when the latter was killed at the first Battle of Newbury, 1643.

William Dobson was pre-eminently the portraitist of the royalist officers of the Civil War. Nothing is known of his earlier career except that, according to the antiquarian writer, Richard Symonds, he was the pupil of Francis Cleyn, the decorative painter. Charles I set up his court at Oxford in October 1642, shortly after the Battle of Edgehill, and it was in Oxford that the bulk of Dobson's known work was done; he died in London in October 1646, at the age of thirty-six, only six months after the king had left his headquarters at Christ Church. Dobson was perceived at the time to be the natural successor of Van Dyck, who had died in 1641, but, although he was thoroughly familiar with Van Dyck's work (and with the great collections of Old Masters formed by the king and his associates before the war) there is no evidence that he was trained in Van Dyck's studio, and his style is far removed from the suave, elegant fluency and sophistication of the great Flemish master (see comparative illustration).

The portrait of Neville demonstrates Dobson's customary alert and robust characterization (natural enough amidst the uncertainties of an essentially military camp), together with his boldness of technique: dry rather than fluid in pigment, rich in texture, vigorous in modelling. Neville is shown wearing a crimson royalist sash over his cuirass; in the background is a vignette of cavalry in action and, immediately behind him a sculptured relief of Mercury and Mars, a typical Dobsonesque conceit reminiscent of the borders designed for the Mortlake tapestries by his master, Francis Cleyn. According to J. Douglas Stewart (review of the Dobson exhibition in the *Canadian Art Review*, vol. 14, 1987, pp. 163–5), the scene represents Mercury as moderation or good counsel, restraining Mars (war), and is symbolic of the need to rein in an impetuous cavalry commander. The rocky ledge in the foreground was added at a late stage in the execution, over Neville's buff coat; composition did not come easily to Dobson, and both the pistol and the dog's head read as accessories rather than as elements in the design.

The breastplate, helmet and wheel-lock pistol are, however, carefully and accurately painted, and are similar to actual examples from the seventeenth-century period owned by the Royal Armouries (information kindly supplied by Guy Wilson, Master of the Armouries) (see comparative illustration).

Provenance: By descent to the Hon. Robin Neville, Audley End, from whom it was purchased, through Agnew's, 1981.

Literature: NACF Report, 1980, pp. 30–2; Malcolm Rogers, *William Dobson 1611–46*, exh. cat., National Portrait Gallery, 1984, no. 20.

Sir Anthony van Dyck: *Thomas Killigrew*
1638
Oil on canvas, 106.1 × 86 (41¾ × 33⅞)
Private Collection

German wheel-lock pistol formerly in the collection of Louis XIII
c. 1620
Royal Armouries, HM Tower of London

7

Arthur Capel, 1st Baron Capel, and his Family

Cornelius Johnson (1593–1661)

Oil on canvas, 160 × 259.1 (63 × 102)
*c.*1641?
Signed l.r.: *Cornelius Jansen fecit*

National Portrait Gallery, London (4759)

Arthur Capel (1604–1649) was a Hertfordshire squire who was raised to the peerage in 1641, became a royalist general in the Civil War, served the king loyally afterwards, and was beheaded for his pains a few weeks after his sovereign. If his eldest son, Arthur, on the left of the picture, can be accepted as ten years old at this time, the portrait may have been painted to mark Capel's elevation to the peerage.

Nothing is known of Cornelius Johnson's training, but he was active as a portraitist by 1617; he tended to specialize in head-and-shoulders portraits in feigned ovals. Johnson, a meticulous craftsman in the Gheeraerts tradition, had none of the dash and sophistication of Van Dyck, but nonetheless he possessed considerable powers of characterization and the ability to depict detail gracefully, giving us, in Sir Oliver Millar's words, a 'vivid picture of the quiet country families of the 1630s'. He left for Holland in 1643.

As Millar points out, Johnson was wholly under Van Dyck's influence in his more ambitious works of the 1630s, and the composition of *The Capel Family* is based almost verbatim on Van Dyck's great portrait of Charles I and Henrietta Maria with their two eldest children, painted in 1632 (see comparative illustration); but the children are strung out along the lower edge of the canvas in a somewhat naive way, the curtains are stiff rather than grand, and the garden is a vignette rather than an integral part of the design. When George Vertue saw the portrait at Cassiobury in 1731 he pronounced that 'the composition and disposition is not equal to his single heads or pictures'. The painting is unusual for the date in depicting a garden in such remarkable detail. Lady Capel (heiress of Charles Morrison of Cassiobury, later the seat of the Earls of Essex) was, however, a talented botanical artist and presumably gardener, and her children inherited her interests; Mary, later Duchess of Beaufort, seen on the right, was to become a distinguished horticulturist, and Henry, the child in his mother's arms, established a garden at Kew which was the forerunner of the present Kew Gardens. This formal Jacobean garden is presumably an accurate representation of the Capels' property at Little Hadham.

Provenance: Painted for Arthur, 1st Baron Capel; by descent to Algernon, 8th Earl of Essex; Cassiobury Park sale, Knight, Frank and Rutley, 12–23 June 1922, 4th day, lot 724, bt. Law; Sir Westrow Hulse; anon. sale, Sotheby's, 7 June 1950, lot 131, bt. Gronau; Seymour, 7th Earl of Wilton; anon. sale, Christie's, 13 March 1970, lot 99, bt. Leggatt on behalf of the National Portrait Gallery.

Literature: Alexander J. Finberg, *A Chronological List of Portraits by Cornelius Johnson*, Walpole Society, vol. 10, 1922, no. 94; *Vertue Note Books*, vol. 4, Walpole Society, vol. 24, 1936, p. 17; Sir Oliver Millar in Margaret Whinney and Oliver Millar, *English Art 1625–1714*, Oxford, 1957, pp. 66–7; NACF Report, 1970, p. 22; Sir Oliver Millar, *The Age of Charles I*, exh. cat., Tate Gallery, 1972, no. 38.

Sir Anthony van Dyck: *Charles I and Queen Henrietta Maria with their two eldest children, Charles, Prince of Wales and Mary, Princess Royal*
1632
Oil on canvas, 370.8 × 274.3 (144⅝ × 107)
Royal Collection, Buckingham Palace, London
(by gracious permission of Her Majesty The Queen)

8

Sir Thomas Aston at the Deathbed of his Wife

John Souch (c.1593–1645)

Oil on canvas, 203.2 × 215.1 ($79\frac{7}{8}$ × $84\frac{5}{8}$)
Signed b.c.: *Jo: Souch/Cestren[s]/Fecit* and dated on the inscription
t.l.: *Septem: 30/16[3]5*

Manchester City Art Gallery

Sir Thomas Aston (1600–1645), who married Magdalene
(daughter of Sir John Poultney of Misterton, Leicestershire), was
Sheriff of Chester in 1635 and led the king's forces in the county
during the Civil War. In 1645 he was captured during the siege of
Chester; imprisoned in Stafford, he died of a fever brought on by
a wound received while trying to escape.

John Souch was apprenticed in Chester in 1607 for a period
of ten years to the heraldic artist, Randle Holme; he later played
a leading role in the affairs of the Chester Painters' Company.
His work is only known, however, from a very small group of
portraits of worthies from that part of England.

This deathbed scene is evidently influenced by heraldic art,
for, although the portraits are evidently likenesses, in style close
to the work of Cornelius Johnson, the picture is not treated
naturalistically – the pose of Sir Thomas is extraordinary enough
– but as an assembly of figures and objects arranged symbolically,
with appropriate Latin inscriptions, illustrative of a particular
event and its place in the family history. In this respect it is
typical of the simple directness of English provincial painting up
to the middle of the eighteenth century, painting which had its
roots in record and, while sometimes not unaccomplished, as in
this case, was often quite uninfluenced by metropolitan traditions
in portraiture (see comparative illustration).

Lady Aston, who died, with her baby, in childbirth on 2 June
1635, is depicted here both on her deathbed and, at the foot of
the bed, seated as she appeared in life but dressed in mourning for
herself and her child. The cradle beside her is draped in black and
under a skull, held over it by Sir Thomas, is the inscription:
Qui Spem carne seminat Metet ossa ['Whoso sows in flesh will reap
bones']. Young Thomas, the couple's only surviving child, who
was to die two years later, is holding a navigational or surveying
instrument in the form of a cross; an inscription beside him refers
to his elder brother, who had died aged three and three-quarters.
A globe and an unstrung lute are on the table. Above, dominating
the whole image, are the coat of arms of Sir Thomas and his wife,
with the inscriptions: *Arescit Coron(e)a mea* ['My garland (crown
of earthly honours) dries up'] and *Virescit post funere virtus* ['Virtue
(my excellence) flourishes after death']. Nonetheless, the eye is
held by the figure of Magdalene slightly offstage, portrayed in the
characteristic Jacobean pose of melancholy, contemplating the
state of death and the state of bereavement and their effects on
the continuity of an established county family.

Provenance: Commissioned by Sir Thomas Aston; thence by descent; Aston
Lodge sale, Brown's of Chester, 1927, lot 239 (as Spanish School, *Death
Scene*), bt. E. Peter Jones, who presented it, through the NACF, 1927.

Literature: NACF Report, 1927, p. 22; C.H. Collins Baker, 'John Souch of
Chester', *Connoisseur*, vol. 80, March 1928, pp. 131–3; Sir Oliver Millar,
The Age of Charles I, exh. cat., Tate Gallery, 1972, no. 148.

Unknown artist: *Sir Henry Unton* (detail)
c. 1596
Oil on panel, 74 × 163.2 ($29\frac{1}{8}$ × $64\frac{1}{4}$)
National Portrait Gallery, London
*The deathbed and funeral scenes from an unusual narrative picture depicting
ten episodes from the life of a distinguished Elizabethan soldier
and diplomat, commissioned by his widow.*

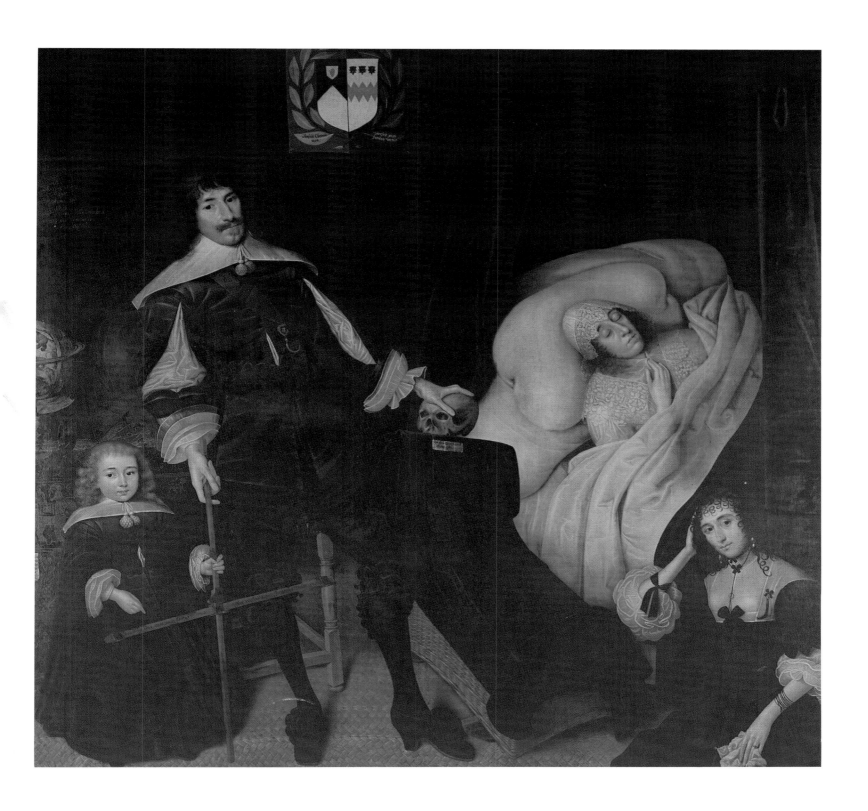

9

Elizabeth, Queen of Bohemia (the 'Winter Queen')

François Dieussart (c.1600–1661)

Marble, 81.6 (32⅕)
Dated on the socle: *1641*

The Board of Trustees of the Victoria & Albert Museum, London
(A8–1967)

Robert Peake the Elder:
Elizabeth, Queen of Bohemia
c. 1610
Oil on canvas, 171.4 × 97.7 (67½ × 38⅛)
National Portrait Gallery, London
This portrait shows Princess Elizabeth about three years
before her marriage.

Elizabeth (1596–1662), daughter of James I and Anne of Denmark, sister of Henry, Prince of Wales, and Charles I, was married to Frederick V, the Elector Palatine (1596–1632), at Whitehall Palace in 1613 (see comparative illustration). Through her youngest daughter, Sophia, who married the Elector of Hanover, she became the ancestress of the Hanoverian kings (George I was her grandson).

The Palatinate, with its court at Heidelberg, was the leading Protestant power within the Holy Roman Empire, and the marriage was intended by the German Protestants to strengthen their alliance against the Catholic Counter Reformation. In 1619 Frederick and Elizabeth were elected King and Queen of Bohemia by a Protestant assembly in rebellion against the Habsburgs, but Habsburg rule was rapidly restored after Frederick's defeat in 1620 at the Battle of the White Mountain, and the couple was forced into exile. Elizabeth spent nearly forty years in Holland; her English income was cut off after the outbreak of the Civil War, and in 1653 she wrote to her generous and devoted friend, Lord Craven, who in the 1630s had fought with the Palatinate forces alongside her sons (the Elector, Charles Louis and her favourite, Prince Rupert), that 'if there be none found [money or credit], I shall have neither meat, nor bread, nor candles'. She returned to England after the Restoration, but died shortly afterwards; Craven, with whom she stayed in London, built her a house at Hamstead Marshall, Berkshire (destroyed by fire in 1718).

François Dieussart, a Flemish sculptor trained in Rome, was one of the ablest and most sensitive of the many artists who worked for Charles I. His first commission, in 1636, was for a colossal monstrance for Henrietta Maria's chapel at Somerset House, which he executed in the full theatrical baroque manner. He left for Holland soon after the outbreak of the Civil War, and his portrait of Elizabeth must have been one of the first commissions he executed at The Hague. Later Dieussart worked in Berlin for the Elector of Brandenburg, and in Brussels and Bruges, where he made busts of Charles II; he may have accompanied the monarch to England at the Restoration, for he died in London in 1661.

There are two versions of the bust of the 'Winter Queen', of which the one kept by the sitter (HRH The Prince of Hanover, Marienburg) is a penetrating characterization of the exiled queen, then in her mid-forties. The bust which may have been intended for Craven is less distinguished: the modelling of the head is firm but less sensitive, and the costume more schematic, with the curls drilled out in a repetitive pattern; Elizabeth is not shown wearing a pearl necklace and, most significantly, her dress is held at the shoulder by a jewelled brooch rather than a medallion bearing a profile portrait of her dead husband, the 'Winter King'. In the Craven collection this bust was paired with one of Elizabeth's daughter, later Electress of Hanover, dating from 1648 (National Portrait Gallery). Dieussart also made busts of Elizabeth's sons, Prince Charles Louis (Arundel Castle), dated 1637, and Prince Rupert (Ashmolean Museum, Oxford).

Provenance: Either given by the sitter to William, 1st Earl of Craven, or bequeathed to him later by Prince Rupert, who inherited many of his mother's possessions; by descent to Cornelia, Countess of Craven; purchased by private treaty sale from the Craven Trustees, 1966.

Literature: NACF Report, 1967, p. 26; Charles Avery, *François Dieussart (c. 1600–61), Portrait Sculptor to the Courts of Northern Europe*, Victoria and Albert Museum Yearbook, no. 4, 1974, pp. 72–4.

ÆLIS·REG·
BOH·
FIL·IAC·REX·MAG
1641

10

Sir John and Lady Cotton with their Son and Daughter

Sir Peter Lely (1618–1680)

Oil on canvas, 157.4 × 225.3 (62 × 88¾)
Inscribed b.l.: *P. Lely P./1660*

Manchester City Art Gallery

Sir John Cotton (1616–1689), of Landwade, Cambridgeshire, was a loyal supporter of Charles I in the Civil War, and was responsible for carrying the Cambridge University plate to the king encamped at Oxford. Cotton married Jane (1634–1692), daughter of Edward Hinde of Madingley Hall. The children in the portrait are Cotton's heir, John (*c.*1649–1712), MP for Cambridge 1689–1708, and his daughter, Jane (1648–1707).

Lely, who studied in Haarlem, came to London during the early years of the Civil War, and painted subject pictures as well as portraits. Already described in 1654 as 'the best artist in England', he was made Principal Painter to the King in 1661, soon after the Restoration, with a stipend of 200 pounds a year, 'as formerly to Sʳ Vandyke'. Regarded by Restoration society as Van Dyck's natural successor, Lely was in general demand and lived in considerable state in the Piazza, Covent Garden, in conscious emulation of the grand London life style of his great predecessor.

In the 1660s Lely was at the height of his powers, and the portrait of the Cotton family, a three-quarter-length group in the Van Dyck tradition (see comparative illustration), executed with assurance throughout in rich, fresh colour, is one of the masterpieces of those years. The group is not idealized: the portraits are evidently excellent likenesses, and the sitters are posed in informal attire, Sir John in a simple black vest and his wife in a night-gown (Lely customarily used a night-gown or shift for his female sitters since the material could be disposed in a lively fashion); the only flourish is in the flowing blue drapery of the Cottons' daughter, who is bringing flowers for her mother to bind into a wreath. The background is as carefully organized and finely painted as the rest of the picture; the animated sculptural group with putti playing is a characteristic feature of Lely's work. The contemporary frame is particularly fine.

Provenance: By descent from the last baronet to Major Affleck King; by descent to the Revd J.S. Brewis; Brewis sale, Sotheby's, 30 November 1966, lot 70, bt. Colnaghi's for Manchester City Art Gallery.

Literature: NACF Report, 1966, p. 23; Sir Oliver Millar, *Sir Peter Lely 1618–80*, exh. cat., National Portrait Gallery, 1978, no. 30.

Sir Anthony van Dyck: *The Family of Endymion Porter*
c. 1633
Oil on canvas, 103.7 × 197.5 (41½ × 79)
Private Collection

11

The Hon. Mary Lowther

Godfried Schalcken (1643–1706)

Oil on canvas, 211.5 × 121 ($83\frac{1}{4}$ × $47\frac{1}{2}$)
c.1692–1695
Signed b.r.: *G. Schalcken*

Sewerby Hall Art Gallery, Bridlington, East Yorkshire Borough
Council (s.a.g. 289.78)

Mary Lowther (died 1706) was the eldest daughter of John, 1st
Viscount Lonsdale, and Catherine Thynne; she married Sir John
Wentworth of Broadsworth and North Elmsall.

Schalcken, a Dordrecht painter who had studied first under
Samuel van Hoogstraten and then under Gerard Dou, came to
England in about 1692, probably encouraged by earlier patronage
from William III, whose portrait he painted. His smoothly
painted biblical, mythological and genre scenes in the manner of
Dou, usually illuminated by candlelight, exuding a warm, red
glow and finished in a high gloss, were immensely popular and
continued to be sought after by eighteenth-century British
collectors, who prized the enamel-like finish of Adriaen van der
Werff. But Schalcken seems to have met with little success as a
portraitist, partly, it is said, because of his boorish manners;
he is last recorded in England in October 1695, and had certainly
returned to Holland by 1699.

Mary Lowther's portrait, the only known full-length by
Schalcken, is first recorded in an inventory of the Lowther Castle
collection in 1696: 'In the withdrawing room my Daughter
Wentworth by Schalcken £20–0–0' (Cumbria County Record
Office). Although the canvas bears an inscription describing the
sitter as 'afterwards wife' to Sir John Wentworth, the evidence of
the inventory indicates that by 1696 Mary was married,
suggesting that the picture was probably a marriage portrait.
The ornamental fountain in the background, symbolic of spiritual
life and salvation, may refer to the responsibilities of matrimony.
Mary is holding a peach in her left hand; the peach and the bunch
of grapes are symbols of fertility. The unclasped dress may have a
similar connotation. But the presence of the parrot needs
explanation. Although parrots had appeared in British portraits
since the beginning of the seventeenth century, perhaps simply
as exotic pets, Desmond Shawe-Taylor has reminded us of Lord
Shaftesbury's advice to painters in 1713, not to introduce
extraneous objects since the audience will read them as if
emblematic. The picture is smoothly painted and the expression
sweetly affectionate; the stately turn of the head is echoed by the
blue drapery, rather meaningless as an item of apparel, drawn
across the sitter's orange satin dress. The Continental polish and
sophistication of Schalcken's portrait are in marked contrast with
the more sober baroque, then prevailing in the styles of Kneller
(see comparative illustration) and Dahl, Closterman and Riley.
But Schalcken's fee of twenty pounds as an unestablished
foreigner was a very great deal less than the fifty pounds which
Kneller, with his busy practice, was able to command at this
period for a full-length portrait.

Provenance: John, 1st Viscount Lonsdale, Lowther Castle, Yorkshire;
Strickland collection, Boynton Hall, near Bridlington, until 1950; Strickland
sale, Sotheby's, 29 November 1978, lot 131, bt. Hugh Trevor Field Art
Fund Trust.

Literature: NACF Report, 1978, pp. 33–4; Thierry Beherman, *Godfried
Schalcken*, Paris, 1988, no. 95.

Sir Godfrey Kneller: *Isabella, Duchess of Grafton*
c. 1690
Oil on canvas, 233 × 143.5 ($91\frac{3}{4}$ × $56\frac{1}{2}$)
Royal Collection, Hampton Court Palace, London
(by gracious permission of Her Majesty The Queen)
*One of the series of 'the principal Ladies attending upon her Majesty', painted
for Queen Mary II, known as the Hampton Court Beauties.*

12

Jacob Tonson I

Sir Godfrey Kneller, Bt. (1649?–1723)

Oil on canvas, 91.4 × 71.1 (36 × 28)
Signed and dated b.r.: *G Kneller/1717* [the GK in monogram]

National Portrait Gallery, London (3230)

Sir Godfrey Kneller:
Charles Seymour, 6th Duke of Somerset
c. 1703
Oil on canvas, 91.4 × 71.1 (36 × 28)
National Portrait Gallery, London

Jacob Tonson (1656?–1736), who made a fortune when he acquired the rights of Milton's *Paradise Lost*, became the leading publisher and bookseller of his day, publishing most of the works of Dryden. When the Kit-cat Club was founded in about 1700, he became its secretary, and for the first few years meetings were held at Christopher Cat's tavern near Temple Bar (the Club was named after Cat's famous mutton pies, known as 'Kit-cats'). Later, it was at his newly acquired house at Barn Elms, Putney, that the members gathered and dined. The Club has been described as 'the Whig party in its social aspect', and included the managers of the party, great Whig landowners, younger politicians like Walpole and Pulteney, and writers and dramatists such as Addison and Steele, Congreve and Vanbrugh, who called it 'the best club that ever met'. The idea of a collection of portraits of members of the Club, to be presented to Tonson, seems to have been the Duke of Somerset's, and he was the first to give Tonson his portrait (see comparative illustration).

Godfrey Kneller was born in Lübeck and travelled in Holland and Italy before settling in England in 1674 or 1675; assured and ambitious, he soon obtained sittings from Charles II, later produced state portraits of James II and Mary of Modena, and, in the new reign, became Principal Painter to William and Mary and was knighted. Inevitably it was Kneller, whose large and efficient practice dominated English portraiture for forty years, who was entrusted with the 'Kit-cat' commissions, though he was not a member of the Club. He had already painted Tonson at full-length in or before 1698 (present whereabouts unknown), and was a near-neighbour at Whitton. The unusual size of the portraits (91.6 × 71.2; 36 × 28), now known as a Kit-cat size, is larger than the standard head-and-shoulders (76.3 × 63.6; 30 × 25); it allowed for the inclusion of hands and greater variety in composition, and was probably dictated by Tonson. The forty-two portraits in the series were displayed in a special room at Barn Elms, and special rooms were built for them by later owners, the last being at Bayfordbury, where they were hung from 1812. The NACF's purchase of the whole set in 1945 is by far the most significant contribution to the study of British portraiture that has ever been made by the Fund. The portraits remain in their original frames, and are displayed chiefly in London but partly at the Gallery's outstation in a National Trust property of the period, Beningbrough Hall, near York.

Of the many splendid characterizations in this remarkable series, Kneller's portrait of Tonson is undoubtedly the most penetrating. As Sir Oliver Millar has written, it has 'an ease, informality, and blunt understanding which anticipate Hogarth'. Tonson is portrayed in a simple turban cap rather than the wig sported by his fellow members; he holds a finely bound copy of *Paradise Lost* in his hand and is leaning slightly forward over the arm of his chair, gazing upwards beyond the spectator with confidence and a certain pugnacity. Dryden characterized Tonson thus: 'With leering looks, bull-faced, and freckled fair;/With two left legs, and Judas-coloured hair,/And frowzy pores, that taint the ambient air.'

Provenance: Painted for the Kit-cat Club collection; by descent, through Jacob Tonson III, to William Baker of Bayfordbury; purchased, with the rest of the collection, by the NACF, and presented, 1945.

Literature: NACF Report, 1945, pp. 18–19; Sir Oliver Millar in Margaret Whinney and Oliver Millar, *English Art 1625–1714*, Oxford, 1957, p. 197; David Piper, *Catalogue of Seventeenth-Century Portraits in the National Portrait Gallery 1625–1714*, Cambridge, 1963, pp. 346–7 and 398–403.

13

Richard Boyle, 3rd Earl of Burlington

Jonathan Richardson the Elder (1665–1745)

Oil on canvas, 146 × 116.8 (57½ × 46)
*c.*1717–1719

National Portrait Gallery, London (4818)

Lord Burlington (1695–1753), a wealthy Yorkshire landowner who had been an admirer since his youth of the architecture of Palladio and Inigo Jones, sought to revive in England the canons of Roman architecture as laid down by Vitruvius and interpreted by Palladio, Scamozzi and Jones; by the 1730s he had become the arbiter of architectural taste and was largely responsible for establishing Palladianism as the accepted style. William Kent, whom he had brought back from Italy in 1719 as a history painter to decorate Burlington House, became the principal disseminator of Burlington's architectural principles from his position at the Board of Works, which the latter had secured for him; Burlington was adept at placing his protégés. An architect as well as a patron (he 'could draw and design as well as pay the bill'), Burlington designed Chiswick House for his own use, and reconstructed Palladio's Egyptian Hall at the Assembly Rooms in York.

Jonathan Richardson was, like Burlington, a man of ideas, and is best known for his *Theory of Painting*, published in 1715, which deeply influenced the young Joshua Reynolds. A pupil of Kneller's more matter-of-fact contemporary, John Riley, Richardson acquired from his teacher the sober and unaffected style which became his hallmark (see comparative illustration). He probably painted his portrait of Lord Burlington soon after the latter had designed his first building, the garden pavilion or 'Bagnio' erected in 1717 in the grounds of old Chiswick House, which is included in the picture; the youthful architect, looking serious and somewhat dour in spite of his showy crimson coat and cap, and resting his arm on a plinth adorned with a coronet and his coat of arms, holds a pair of dividers in his right hand.

Provenance: Anon. sale, Sotheby's, 28 July 1954, lot 137 (as by Francis Hayman), bt. Colefax and Fowler; Mrs C.G. Lancaster, from whom it was purchased, 1970.

Literature: NACF Report, 1970, p. 20; John Kerslake, *Early Georgian Portraits*, National Portrait Gallery, 1977, vol. 1, p. 29.

John Riley: *John Dryden*
c. 1685
Oil on canvas, 122 × 91.4 (48 × 36)
Traquair House

Earl of Burlington.

14

The Graham Children

William Hogarth (1697–1764)

Oil on canvas, 160.5 × 181 (63¼ × 71¼)
Signed and dated t.r.: *W. Hogarth pinx. 1742.*

The Trustees of the National Gallery, London (4756)

Richard Robert Graham (1734–1816), the eight- or nine-year-old boy on the right of the picture, was the son of Daniel Graham, Apothecary to Chelsea Hospital, a post to which he succeeded, employing a practising apothecary to carry out the duties. Nothing is known about his three sisters.

Hogarth, a 'rough diamond' of deprived background (his father was imprisoned for debt, and the family lived within the Rules of the Fleet Prison for five years), was an energetic and profoundly ambitious painter-engraver who played a leading role in every aspect of artistic life and production in Britain in the second quarter of the eighteenth century. Founder of the St Martin's Lane Academy, and promoter of the Foundling Hospital state rooms and Vauxhall Gardens (both popular rendezvous) as a forum for displaying the best in British painting, he executed pictures of the metropolis with vivid, usually low-life, narrative; history paintings; conversation pieces; and theatre scenes. He also developed a new genre known as the 'modern moral subject' – a series of pictures satirizing the moral standards and abuses of the day, of which *A Rake's Progress* (Sir John Soane's Museum) is one example – which he engraved with the intention of reaching the widest possible audience.

In 1740 Hogarth painted his full-length of Captain Coram (Foundling Hospital), 'this mighty portrait' as he called it, to demonstrate that the fashionable French immigrant, Jean-Baptiste van Loo, did not rule the roost; and during the first half of the 1740s he was especially active as a portraitist on the scale of life.

The Graham Children, a conversation piece raised to this level (see comparative illustration), is one of his most ambitious and successful canvases of this date.

Hogarth's remarkable gift for individual characterization certainly did not stop short of children. Richard is playing a bird organ to a canary in a gilded cage, also the object of the family cat's preying eyes; his elder sister evidently sees herself as the 'grown-up' in charge, and is holding the hand of the child in an elaborate baby carriage, who covets the cherries she is dangling in her left hand; his other sister is smiling to herself and practising a curtsey. The painting is full of incident, the picture surface scattered with detail, bright local colour and highlights in a manner characteristic of rococo art. The dominant rhythm is the serpentine line, formed by the older girls' aprons, 'that leads the eye a wanton kind of chace' as Hogarth expressed it in his *Analysis of Beauty*, 1753. But even in this delightful glimpse of middle-class childhood Hogarth cannot avoid moralizing. Shawe-Taylor demonstrates that the work is replete with emblematic content. As he points out, everything in the picture – the flowers in the girls' mob-caps, the dress embroidered with flowers, the cherries, the still-life in the corner, the dove ornamenting the baby carriage – 'suggests blossoming loveliness and the promise of love'. But the cupid who has seized the reaper's scythe on the bracket clock, and the painting of a tempest on the back wall, remind us of the evanescence of these youngsters' lives, and takes us back to the tradition of the seventeenth-century Vanitas painting.

Provenance: Richard Graham, who sold it, probably in 1816, to William Seguier (a picture restorer, later first Keeper of the National Gallery), from whom it was purchased by George Watson Taylor; Taylor sale, Erlstoke Mansion, Devizes, 24 July 1832, lot 50, bt. Welbore Ellis, 2nd Earl of Normanton; by descent to Edward, 5th Earl of Normanton, from whom it was bought by Lord Duveen of Millbank and presented, 1934.

Literature: NACF Report, 1934, pp. 39–40; National Gallery Report, 1934, p. 5; Mary Webster, *Hogarth*, 1978, p. 118; Desmond Shawe-Taylor, *The Georgians: Eighteenth-Century Portraiture & Society*, 1990, pp. 209–12.

William Hogarth: *The House of Cards*
1730
Oil on canvas, 63.5 × 76 (25 × 30)
National Museum of Wales

15

Isaac Ware

Louis François Roubiliac (1705?–1762)

Marble, 50.5 (19⅞) high
*c.*1755–1762

National Portrait Gallery, London (4982)

Isaac Ware (died 1766) was of humble origins but, showing an early talent for drawing, he was encouraged by a patron, possibly Lord Burlington, who sent him to Italy to study architecture. Like Henry Flitcroft, he furthered the Palladian movement in British architecture through the official positions he subsequently held, for nearly forty years, on the Board of Works. Sir John Summerson has written (letter in the National Portrait Gallery Registry) that he was 'a man of real intellectual calibre and an original designer'; his *Complete Body of Architecture*, 1735, to which Sir William Chambers owed much, was an influential textbook. Ware's most important works in private practice were Chesterfield House, South Audley Street, built for Lord Chesterfield, 1749 (demolished 1937), and Wrotham Park, Middlesex, built for Admiral Byng, 1754.

Ware frequented Old Slaughter's coffee-house in St Martin's Lane, and would thus have been well acquainted with the avant-garde artists of the English Rococo, aptly christened by Mark Girouard 'the St Martin's Lane set' on account of their association with the St Martin's Lane Academy and their invigoration of the *quartier*. Roubiliac, born in Lyon and trained under Nicolas Coustou, who had settled in London before 1735, established his reputation with the celebrated statue of Handel for Vauxhall Gardens (Victoria and Albert Museum) and was one of the principal figures in this group. He was in every way the opposite of Rysbrack, his great contemporary in the medium, who was a much broader, idealizing, and often classicizing, artist (see comparative illustration); and the bust of Ware, with its sharp turn of the head, giving a sense of immediacy, individual characterization, and soft, naturalistic treatment of the cap – the equivalent in sculpture of the lively naturalism of Hogarth – is an excellent example of his style. Although it is not in fact of the highest quality in terms of Roubiliac's technical skill, John Thomas Smith, Nollekens's biographer, who in 1802 engraved a drawing of the clay model, described this bust as one of the sculptor's 'best performances'. (Smith's father, Nathaniel, Roubiliac's apprentice from 1755, had seen the work in progress.) The bust was overlooked until Howard Colvin discovered it in the mid-1950s. Roubiliac executed an earlier bust of Ware (Detroit Institute of Arts), which George Vertue saw in 1741 and described as 'extreamly like'. This version, formerly at Ripley Castle, Yorkshire, is much more sharply characterized, and such details as the buttonholes in the collar and the incised pupils of the eyes confirm its status as the prime original (I owe this information to Howard Colvin and to Alan Phipps Darr, Curator of European Sculpture and Decorative Arts, Detroit Institute of Arts).

Provenance: Richard Wellesley; with Cyril Humphris, from whom it was purchased, after export deferral, 1974.

Literature: Vertue Note Books, vol. 3, Walpole Society, vol. 22, 1934, p. 105; Howard Colvin, 'Roubiliac's Bust of Isaac Ware', *Burlington Magazine*, vol. 97, May 1955, p. 151; NACF Report, 1974, p. 10.

John Rysbrack: *Bust of Peter Tillemans*
1727
Terracotta bust, 53.7 × 45 (21½ × 18)
Yale Center for British Art, Paul Mellon Collection,
partial gift of Cyril Humphris

16

Edward and Mary Macro

Peter Tillemans (*c*.1684–1734)

Oil on canvas, 117.2 × 88.1 (46⅛ × 34¾)
c.1733
Signed b.l.: *Peter Tillemans F*

Norwich Castle Museum, Norfolk Museums Service (21.1.991)

Edward (died 1766) and Mary Macro (1719–1775) were the children of the Revd Dr Cox Macro, of Little Haugh Hall, near Bury St Edmunds, who was chaplain to George II. Cox Macro had inherited a fortune and became a scholar and antiquary, forming an extensive collection of pictures, coins and medals, books and manuscripts; he was Tillemans' principal patron. Young Edward became a soldier and died abroad during his father's lifetime. Mary married William Staniforth of Sheffield in 1767, three months after the death of her father, who had opposed the union; she was then too old to have children.

Peter Tillemans, an Antwerp-trained painter, came to England in 1708 (see comparative illustration), and became a member of Kneller's newly-formed Academy of Painting in 1711; in 1725 he served as steward of the exclusive (but increasingly moribund) Society of St Luke, described by George Vertue as 'the Tip top Clubb of all, for men of the highest Character in Arts & Gentlemen Lovers of Art'. Best known for his Newmarket scenes and views of the Thames, Tillemans was a versatile but chiefly sporting painter, who travelled widely in England, painting views of country houses. In 1733–1734 he was employed on painting a series of overdoors and overmantels for Macro at Little Haugh Hall when he died there suddenly, leaving an overmantel of a horse with groom and hounds unfinished. His patron commissioned a bust of him from Rysbrack (Yale Center for British Art, New Haven; see p. 62) within weeks of his death.

The double portrait of Macro's two children was executed during Tillemans' final stay at their home. Part of the formal garden, with clipped hedge and classical summerhouse, is seen in the background. Tillemans' natural fluency of handling is evident in the Watteauesque treatment of Mary's dress, and his skill as an animal painter in his portraits of the children's favourite dogs, a whippet, a spaniel and a pug – the three most popular breeds for domestic pets at that time. Characteristic of the age, though, as usual, Hogarth rebelled against the concept (see no. 14), in which the youngsters are treated as young adults rather than as children. Edward, as fashionably dressed as his sister, is clasping a smart tricorn hat under his arm; Mary has feathers and a sprig of flowers in her hair and is holding a bunch of flowers in her lap. This fresh and charming portrait anticipates the dainty conversation pieces of Tillemans' pupil, Arthur Devis, but is much livelier in its handling.

Provenance: Revd Dr Cox Macro; thence by descent to Philippa and Charity Patteson, from whom it was purchased, with the rest of the Patteson collection, 1991.

Literature: Robert Raines, 'Peter Tillemans, Life and Work', *The Walpole Society*, vol. 47, 1980, no. 79; to be published in the NACF Review for 1992.

Exhibitions: Manners & Morals: Hogarth and British Painting 1700–1760, Tate Gallery, 1987–8, no. 45; *Dutch and Flemish Painting in Norfolk*, Castle Museum, Norwich, 1988, no. 82.

Peter Tillemans: *The Artist's Studio*
c. 1716
Oil on canvas, 68.3 × 84 (27 × 33)
Norfolk Museums Service (Norwich Castle Museum)

17

The Duet

Arthur Devis (1712–1787)

Oil on canvas, 115.8 × 103.7 (45½ × 40¾)
Signed and dated on the stretcher of the harpsichord
l.r.: *Art.* *Devis fe. 1749*

The Board of Trustees of the Victoria & Albert Museum, London
(P.31–1955)

Hogarth popularized the conversation piece, making it a
fashionable novelty in the early 1730s (see comparative
illustration). But when the vogue had slipped in the social scale,
it was Arthur Devis, a native of Preston who had settled in
London by 1742, who devoted himself almost exclusively to these
small-scale portraits in domestic surroundings. From his studio in
Great Queen Street he carried on a successful practice with
middle-class sitters for about twenty years, until his largely
unchanging and highly artificial style was eclipsed in the 1760s by
the greater sophistication of Zoffany. Joseph Burke, in his *Oxford
History*, has accurately characterized Devis's 'essentially ... doll's
house world ... His interiors have the rectilinear neatness and
dovetailing precision of the model cabinet-maker's masterwork;
his landscapes could be cut out for a toy theatre; and his
silhouette figures positively invite the scissors.'

Nothing is known about the sitters in this picture and, as in
all Devis's paintings (with a single exception), the room, typically
bereft of furniture, with an expanse of bare floor, is probably the
artist's own invention. Nonetheless, equally typically, the setting
is devised to reflect the sitters' social aspirations: fashionable
Italianate landscapes adorn the wall; the Venetian window
characteristic of the English Palladian movement is taken from an
architectural pattern book; and there is a hint of a gentleman's
park beyond. Everything in the picture down to the floorboards,
but notably the musical instruments, is meticulously delineated.
As always with Devis, the costume is colourful and lovingly
painted. Although the couple are engaged in a duet – the man
has put down his violin and is handing the woman, presumably
his wife, a sheet of music, which she is about to take from him –
both are involved with the spectator rather than with each other.
The emphasis is on possessions, gentility and status rather than
any kind of action.

Provenance: Cecil Fane de Salis; de Salis sale, Christie's, 11 March 1932,
lot 97, bt. Gooden & Fox for Ernest E. Cook, who bequeathed it
(with the rest of his collection) to the NACF; allocated 1955.

Literature: NACF Report, 1955, p. 35; Ellen G. d'Oench, *The Conversation
Piece: Arthur Devis & His Contemporaries*, exh. cat., Yale Center for British
Art, New Haven, 1980, no. 22; Stephen Sartin in *Polite Society*, exh. cat.,
Harris Museum and Art Gallery, Preston, and National Portrait Gallery,
1983, no. 17.

William Hogarth: *A Performance of 'The Indian Emperor or
The Conquest of Mexico by the Spaniards'*
1732–1735
Oil on canvas, 131 × 146.7 (51½ × 57¾)
Private Collection

18

Sir Roger and Lady Bradshaigh

Edward Haytley (active *c*.1740–1760)

Oil on canvas, 67 × 87 (26½ × 34¼)
Inscribed b.r.: *Heatly Pinx*ᵗ *1746*

Heritage Service, Wigan Metropolitan Borough Council
(B81.909)

Sir Roger Bradshaigh (died 1787), of Haigh Hall, Lancashire (seen in the background of the picture), came from a family which had owned Haigh Hall for centuries, and was closely connected with Wigan both as Members of Parliament and as leaders in developing its coal industry. Sir Roger was the fourth and last baronet, and after his death the estate was inherited by his great-niece, who married Alexander, 6th Earl of Balcarres. The 24th Earl of Crawford demolished the Elizabethan house and built the present Hall, 1827–1835. The stable block has recently been renovated as a museum to accommodate temporary exhibitions.

Edward Haytley, whose conversation pieces and portraits-in-little have traditionally been attributed to Arthur Devis, has only recently been identified as an artist with a distinct personality of his own. He painted with a meticulous touch similar to that of Devis, but his compositions, often panoramic landscapes, are packed with detail and at the same time more coherent (see comparative illustration).

In this small but richly descriptive canvas Sir Roger and Lady Bradshaigh are dressed partially in Van Dyck costume, a fashionable conceit of the period; as in pictures by Devis, he is gesturing towards, but not looking at, his wife, Dorothy, and has his other hand on his telescope, a familiar motif in Haytley's canvases but nonetheless evidently a prized possession; his spaniel gazes up at him, and his wife, who is looking out at the spectator, holds a book in her hand, an accessory that illustrates what was significant in her life, just as the telescope reveals her husband's preoccupations. As Harris points out, the house had been refenestrated and the wing at the rear to the left reduced in height and rebuilt since the property was engraved for Knyff and Kip's *Nouveau Thêatre de La Grande Bretagne*, 1708. The elegant wooden or iron-paled staircase looks as though it has only recently been constructed as an embellishment to the formal terraced garden, now bereft of its topiary, and there is a modish Gothick ruin on the hill. The picture is a record of wealth dispensed in keeping *au courant* with metropolitan fashion, and was proudly hung in the Bradshaighs' London house where everyone could see it.

Dorothy Bradshaigh was a great admirer of the novelist Samuel Richardson, with whom she carried on an anonymous correspondence, only meeting him as a result of a visit to Joseph Highmore's studio to see that artist's paintings illustrating

Arthur Devis: *Robert Gwillym, of Atherton, and his Family*
c. 1745–1746
Oil on canvas, 101.5 × 127 (39⅝ × 50)
Yale Center for British Art, Paul Mellon Collection

Sr. Roger & Lady Bradshaigh   Heatly Pinx.t 1746

Richardson's *Pamela* (Highmore's principal claim to fame). In March 1750 Richardson asked Lady Bradshaigh's permission to have a copy painted by Highmore of the Haytley 'that hangs over your chimey in New Bond Street. You know not the pleasure I shall have in looking upon it, when you are at that seat, which is there drawn in so lively a manner, and is so very delightful'. In return Lady Bradshaigh asked for a replica of Highmore's portrait of Richardson. Both pictures were evidently painted promptly, as Highmore's portrait (see comparative illustration), which shows his copy of the Haytley in the background, is dated 1750.

Provenance: Painted for Sir Roger Bradshaigh; probably passed to his sister-in-law, Elizabeth Echlin; thence by descent to the MacKinnon of MacKinnon; MacKinnon sale, Sotheby's, 12 November 1980, lot 29, bt. Baskett and Day, from whom it was purchased, 1981.

Literature: John Harris, *The Artist and the Country House*, 1979, pp. 165 and 219 (as attributed to Joseph Highmore); NACF Report, 1981, pp. 61–3; Stephen Sartin in *Polite Society*, exh. cat., Harris Museum and Art Gallery, Preston, and National Portrait Gallery, 1983, no. 54; Alyson Wilson in *Prospects of Town and Park*, exh. cat., Colnaghi's, 1988, no. 11.

Joseph Highmore: *Samuel Richardson*
1750
Oil on canvas, 52.7 × 36.8 (20¾ × 14½)
National Portrait Gallery, London

19

Self-portrait of the Artist (Francis Hayman) at his Easel

Francis Hayman (1708–1776)

Oil on canvas, 60.7 × 43.5 (23⅞ × 17⅛)
1750

Royal Albert Memorial Museum, Exeter (99/1953)

Francis Hayman, a close friend and associate of Hogarth, and a teacher of Gainsborough, was a member of the avant-garde circle of artists centred on the St Martin's Lane Academy which, in the 1730s and 1740s, spread the gaiety, artifice and sensuousness of the rococo style in Britain. Like Hogarth, his range was wide, embracing decorative and scene painting, history and mythological pictures, illustrations to literature, theatre scenes, conversation pieces and small full-length portraits; like Hogarth, too, he drew his patronage from professional, cultural and artistic circles rather than from the aristocratic beau monde. He is chiefly renowned for the numerous pictures he painted to help keep London's most celebrated pleasure garden, Vauxhall Gardens, *à la page*: large canvases of rural pastimes and children's games for the supper boxes and, later, four immense history paintings (now lost) commemorating the victories of the Seven Years War.

This self-portrait was painted as a companion to a portrait Hayman had done of Sir Edward Littleton, of Teddesley Hall, Staffordshire (see comparative illustration), a patron of Rysbrack and friend of James West (see no. 25) and Cox Macro (see no. 16). Both in its informality of posture and design and in the lively, rippling highlights of the morning-gown it is a typically rococo work.

Provenance: Believed to have been a gift from the artist to Sir Edward Littleton; by descent to Edward, 5th Baron Hatherton; Hatherton sale, Christie's, 6 November 1953, lot 7 (without attribution), bt. Davey; presented by the NACF, 1953.

Literature: NACF Report, 1953, p. 20; Brian Allen, *Francis Hayman*, exh.cat., Yale Center for British Art, New Haven, and Iveagh Bequest, Kenwood, 1987, no. 21.

Francis Hayman: *Sir Edward Littleton*
1750
Oil on canvas, 59 × 40.6 (23¼ × 16)
Private Collection

20

George Michael Moser and his wife, Mary

Carl Marcus Tuscher (active second quarter of the eighteenth century)

Oil on canvas, 72 × 73 (28⅜ × 28¾)
c.1742–1743

Geffrye Museum Trust, London (70/1979)

Sir George Scharf: *George Michael Moser and his wife, Mary*
1865
Pen and ink, 14.8 × 9.3 (6 × 4)
National Portrait Gallery Archive

Carl Marcus Tuscher: *The Shudi Family*
c. 1742
Oil on canvas, 83.4 × 141.5 (32¾ × 55¾)
National Portrait Gallery, London

Until late in 1984 this charming portrait was attributed to a variety of artists active in England in the second quarter of the eighteenth century. Then Gavin Graham, on a visit to Copenhagen, where he saw a number of portraits by Tuscher, made the connection. The identification of the sitters was established by a drawing by Sir George Scharf, the first director of the National Portrait Gallery, who examined the picture on 2 February 1858 and made a careful drawing of the figures (see comparative illustration). The lady was then identified as Moser's daughter, Mary (later Mrs Lloyd). George Michael Moser (1704–1783), born in Schaffhausen, the son of an eminent Swiss engineer and metal-worker, and educated in Geneva, came to England in 1726 and rose to be the leading gold-chaser and enameller of his day; a man of 'amiable disposition', according to Sir Joshua Reynolds, he was much esteemed by George III and Queen Charlotte. As Treasurer and virtual manager of the St Martin's Lane Academy he was instrumental in establishing the Royal Academy and was elected its first Keeper.

The little-known German artist and architect, Carl Marcus Tuscher, was born in Nuremberg, where he was taught by Johan Daniel Preisler, and left for Italy in 1728 with Preisler's son; he remained in Italy for thirteen years, becoming a member of the Academy in Florence, before travelling in 1741 to London. Vertue called him 'a Man of general genious excellent at drawing Views places of Buildings &c. figures of great Variety & composition, very masterly.' Tuscher was summoned to Copenhagen in 1743 and became court painter to Christian VI.

The conversation piece with an outdoor setting was introduced into England in the mid-1720s by Philippe Mercier; but the chief practitioners of portraits-in-little in landscapes or gardens in the 1740s were Arthur Devis and (on this scale) Francis Hayman. The Mosers, he wearing a splendid royal blue morning-gown, are set in a niche in a formal garden with statuary; the prominent bust, upper right, seems to be a portrait (Tuscher employed a similar motif in the group portrait he painted in Leghorn in 1737 [Statens Museum for Kunst, Copenhagen]). The dog at Mary's feet symbolizes fidelity; the flowers signify spring and may refer to future childbirth. Moser married Mary Guymer on 31 January 1729/30, and their son, George, was born on 15 March 1731/2. Their daughter, Mary, however, later the well-known flower painter, was born in 1744, not long after this picture was painted. The rococo rhythms, the crisp contours and sculptural treatment of the costume, the bright colours, and the luscious paint surface are all characteristic of Tuscher's few known works (see comparative illustration). Edwards, writing in 1808, pronounced that 'the picture has more merit than is generally found in the works of the artists of that day.'

Provenance: Mary Lloyd (Moser's daughter); George Cubitt (later 1st Baron Ashcombe) by 1868; anon. sale, Sotheby's, 1972; with Oscar and Peter Johnson, from whom it was purchased, 1974 (as unidentified and attributed to Francis Hayman).

Literature: Edward Edwards, *Anecdotes of Painters*, 1808, p. 2; NACF Report, 1974, p. 9; Jeffery Daniels, 'A Newly Identified Portrait of George Michael Moser', NACF Magazine, Summer 1985, pp. 10–12; Brian Allen, 'Carl Marcus Tuscher: A German Artist in London', *Apollo*, vol. 122, July 1985, pp. 34–5.

Mr and Mrs Robert Andrews

Thomas Gainsborough (1727–1788)

Oil on canvas, 69.8 × 119.4 (27½ × 47)
c.1748–1749

The Trustees of the National Gallery, London (6301)

Robert Andrews (1726?–1806), of Auberies, near Bulmer, in Suffolk, close to Gainsborough's birthplace, married Frances Mary Carter (*c*.1732–1780), of Ballingdon House, Sudbury, at All Saints Church, Sudbury, on 10 November 1748. The picture, which can be dated about 1748 on stylistic grounds, is almost certainly a marriage portrait; the sheaves of stooked corn are a traditional symbol of fertility. Gainsborough also painted a double portrait with landscape background of Frances' parents, Mr and Mrs William Carter; this portrait, a little earlier in date, was sold by the Andrews family in 1920 and was only rediscovered a few years ago.

Gainsborough studied under the French illustrator and engraver, Herbert Gravelot, and much of his very early work must have been associated with illustration and the decorative arts; but his main love was landscape and, when he set up his own studio in 1745, 'his first efforts were small landscapes, which he frequently sold to the dealers at trifling prices'. *Mr and Mrs Robert Andrews* must have been one of the first pictures Gainsborough painted after his return to Sudbury from London in 1748. It is also the undoubted masterpiece of this period. Gainsborough has transformed the tradition of the portrait-in-little with landscape setting by giving the landscape equal importance in the composition. Nor is the landscape in any sense a backdrop, as in other works of Gainsborough's Suffolk years (see comparative illustration). It is a view of the young squire's up-to-date estate at Auberies (notice such significant details as the cattle shelter almost hidden on the left of the canvas), freely and exquisitely brushed, with a truth of tone and atmosphere unique in British landscape painting at that time; the church tower in the background has been identified as that of St Peter's, Sudbury. The dog, the costume, and such details as the catch of the gun are equally beautifully and naturalistically painted. Gainsborough's training in the rococo milieu of the St Martin's Lane avant-garde can be detected in the fashionable twisting shapes of the garden seat and the fretted contours of the clouds rolling across the horizon. The couple are set against a sturdy oak, Robert in the cross-legged pose typical of early Georgian portraiture, with gun and game-bag under his arm, his sixteen-year-old wife sitting pertly beside him in a blue satin dress, the unfinished area of canvas in her lap perhaps intended to be completed with a pheasant shot by her husband.

Provenance: By descent to G.W. Andrews; Andrews sale, Sotheby's, 23 March 1960, lot 59, bt. Agnew's, from whom it was purchased, 1960.

Exhibitions: The picture has been frequently exhibited since it first became generally known after its appearance in the Gainsborough bicentenary exhibition at Ipswich in 1927, but chiefly at *Thomas Gainsborough*, Tate Gallery, 1953, no. 5; *Gainsborough*, Grand Palais, Paris, 1981, no. 4.

Literature: Ellis Waterhouse, *Gainsborough*, London, 1958, no. 18; NACF Report, 1960, pp. 12–13; John Hayes, *Gainsborough: Paintings and drawings*, 1975, p. 203; Desmond Shawe-Taylor, *The Georgians: Eighteenth-Century Portraiture & Society*, 1990, pp. 128–30.

Thomas Gainsborough: *Heneage Lloyd and his Sister* (?)
Early 1750s
Oil on canvas, 64.1 × 81 (25¼ × 31⅞)
Fitzwilliam Museum, Cambridge

22

Admiral Sir George Pocock

Thomas Hudson (1701–1779)

Oil on canvas, 126 × 99.5 (49½ × 39)
Signed and dated b.r.: *T Hudson* [the TH in monogram]/*1749*

Royal Naval Museum, Portsmouth (482/86)

George Pocock (1706–1792) had a long and successful naval career, and was knighted in 1761 when he became an Admiral of the Blue. The crowning achievement of his career was the capture of Havana in 1762, which placed the West Indies securely in British hands.

Thomas Hudson, the son-in-law of Jonathan Richardson, was the most prosperous portrait painter in London from the time Jean Baptiste van Loo returned to Paris in 1742 until the early 1750s. The young Reynolds, a fellow Devonian, was apprenticed to him in 1740, although he only served three years of his four-year term. The hallmarks of Hudson's style are a hard-edged treatment of the image and smooth modelling of the flesh tones, producing a rather bland, mask-like countenance. He was assisted, like Allan Ramsay, by a highly competent drapery painter, Joseph van Aken (see comparative illustration).

The year 1749, when the portrait of Pocock was painted, was an exceptionally busy one for Hudson; it was also a time when the smooth running of his studio was interrupted, in July, by the death of the indispensable Van Aken. Regular naval uniform was introduced in 1748, and Pocock is depicted in the dark blue coat with blue braid, and white waistcoat with similar blue braid, of a flag officer. Rocks and a warship at sea fill out the picture. Hudson's consistently matter-of-fact treatment in this portrait may be compared with Reynolds's softer and more painterly handling in work of the same date (no. 26). Hudson painted Pocock a second time after his knighthood in 1761.

Provenance: M. Knoedler & Co., New York; F. Gonzalez de la Fuente, Mexico City; with Colnaghi's, from whom it was purchased, 1986.

Literature: John Martin Robinson in *The British Face*, exh. cat., Colnaghi's, 1986, no. 19; NACF Review, 1987, p. 161.

Joseph van Aken: *Study of a Lady standing against a Curtain*
1740–1745
Black and white chalk touched with red,
34 × 25.4 (13⅜ × 10)
National Galleries of Scotland, Edinburgh

23

Edward Harvey

Allan Ramsay (1713–1784)

Oil on canvas, 127.3 × 101.6 (50 × 40)
Signed and dated b.r.: *A. Ramsay. 1747.*

Dundee Art Galleries and Museums (40/1953)

Edward Harvey (born 1718), who served as an aide-de-camp to the notorious Duke of Cumberland at the Battle of Culloden, 1746, is portrayed here wearing a scarlet military coat over fashionable civilian dress.

Allan Ramsay, perhaps typically for a Scotsman with an intellectual and literary bent, was one of the few British portraitists of the first half of the eighteenth century to have studied abroad, which he did under Imperiali in Rome and Solimena in Naples (see comparative illustration). By 1739 he had settled in London, and was evidently soon in good practice, for he claimed in 1740: 'I have put all your Vanlois and Soldis and Ruscas to flight and now play the first fiddle myself.' Ramsay's best work is marked by sound draughtsmanship and technique and an unerring sense of tone and colour as well as a delicate naturalness, especially in his later portraits of women, for which he is generally admired.

Ramsay was not especially inventive in his compositions, and his portrait of Harvey is conventional in its arrangement; the device of drawing back the coat to reveal the embroidery on the waistcoat is a common feature not only of his own work but also that of Hudson, and he repeated the whole design in another portrait done the same year. Nonetheless, the individual personality of the sitter is in no way obscured by the stock pattern. One of Ramsay's sitters, Peter Manigault, wrote in 1751 of his portrait: ''Tis done by one of the best hands in England, and is accounted by all judges here, not only an exceeding good likeness, but a very good piece of painting.' George Vertue, who visited Ramsay's studio in August of that year, pronounced Hudson the most employed, but Ramsay 'much superior in merit than other portrait painters – his mens pictures strong likeness firm in drawing – and true flesh colouring natural tinctures his Lady delicate and Genteel – easy free likeness. their habits and dresses well disposed and airy. his flesh tender his silks & satins &c. shineing beautiful & clean – with great Variety.' It was Ramsay who was the only serious rival to Reynolds in the 1750s.

Provenance: By descent, through Harvey's nephew, Sir Eliab Harvey, to his daughter, Georgina Drummond; Barclay Hogarth, 1947; purchased by the NACF and presented, 1952.

Literature: Alastair Smart, *The Life and Art of Allan Ramsay*, 1952, p. 55; NACF Report, 1953, p. 20.

Allan Ramsay: *Samuel Torriano*
1738
Oil on canvas, 76 × 63.5 (30 × 25)
Private Collection

24

William and Hannah Wilberforce

Joseph Highmore (1691–1780)

Oil on canvas, 102.4 × 127.5 (39½ × 49½)
c.1750
Signed c.l.: *Jos. Highmore/Pinx:*

Wilberforce House: Hull City Museums and Art Galleries
(KINCM 194.65)

The sitters have been identified since the picture's acquisition by Hull as William and Hannah Wilberforce, of Wimbledon, the uncle and aunt of William Wilberforce, the philanthropist and parliamentarian who led the cause for the abolition of slavery; it was with them that the young William went to live on the death of his father in 1768.

Joseph Highmore, a portrait painter who worked first in the City, set himself up in Lincoln's Inn Fields in 1724. Like Gainsborough in his early and middle years, he maintained a busy practice without studio assistance and, probably for this reason, avoided full-length portraits. He kept up with the artistic developments of his day, and was influenced successively by Mercier, Hogarth, Van Loo, Ramsay and Reynolds. His portraits-in-little, dainty in pose and gesture and delicate in colour, have something of the quality of rococo porcelain, and his most outstanding work is a masterpiece of the English Rococo – the series of twelve narrative paintings illustrating Samuel Richardson's *Pamela*, engraved in 1745 (see comparative illustration). Highmore was an artist with learned and literary tastes, who kept up a lifelong friendship with Richardson (see no. 18).

The Wilberforce picture is probably a marriage portrait. Pearls, which Hannah is wearing across her breast and entwined in her hair, are the attribute of Margaret of Antioch, the patron saint of childbirth. Flowers are the attribute of spring, and the bunch which Hannah is holding may also allude to a hoped-for birth. William has his hand tucked into his waistcoat in the manner approved by contemporary etiquette books. The work is executed with a fresh, creamy touch characteristic of Highmore's attractive handling of paint.

Provenance: Wilberforce family, of Markington, near Leeds; by descent to W.B. Wilberforce; Wilberforce sale, Christie's, 16 December 1911, lot 89 (as William Wilberforce, grandfather of the philanthropist, and his wife, Sarah Thornton), bt. Coureaw; the Hon. Mrs B.H. Burns; Burns sale, Sotheby's, 20 March 1963, lot 164, bt. Agnew's for Wilberforce House, Hull.

Literature: NACF Report, 1963, p. 20; Alison Shepherd Lewis, *Joseph Highmore: 1692–1780*, Harvard University Ph.D. dissertation, 1975 (Xerox University Microfilms, Ann Arbor, Michigan, 1976), vol. 2, no. 188.

Joseph Highmore: *Pamela telling Nursery Tales*
c. 1744
Oil on canvas, 62.6 × 75.6 (24⅝ × 29¾)
Fitzwilliam Museum, Cambridge

25

William Shakespeare

John Michael Rysbrack (1694–1770)

Marble, 58.5 (23) high
Signed and dated on the back: *Mich^l: Rysbrack. Sculp^t:/1760.*

Birmingham City Museums and Art Gallery (1987.P2)

Peter Scheemakers: *Shakespeare Monument* (detail)
c. 1740
Marble
Westminster Abbey, London

James West, Joint Secretary to the Treasury, 1741–1762, a distinguished bibliophile, collector and antiquary who was elected President of the Royal Society in 1768, decided to convert his country home, Alscot Park, near Stratford-upon-Avon, into what Horace Walpole would have called 'a little plaything house' in the Gothick taste, 1750–1752; after his retirement from the Treasury, he enlarged the house, 1763–1769. The proximity of Alscot to Stratford made a portrait of Shakespeare an appropriate choice for the newly created interior, and the remains of an inscription – *Genio Loci* – are traceable on the bust.

Michael Rysbrack, trained in Antwerp as a sculptor in the classical tradition revived by Duquesnoy, came to England in 1720 and worked with James Gibbs and in Lord Burlington's circle. His most ambitious tomb sculpture, the monument to the Duke of Marlborough (Blenheim Palace chapel) was designed by Kent. In good practice as a portrait sculptor, Rysbrack executed a considerable number of posthumous portraits, chiefly of British historical figures, but mostly early in his career; he made a bust of Shakespeare for the Temple of British Worthies at Stowe in 1732. By 1759 Rysbrack had executed a terracotta of Shakespeare as one of a series of about a dozen busts to decorate the study of one of his principal patrons, Sir Edward Littleton; Rysbrack wrote in November of that year that West 'likes it so well that I am going to do it for him in Marble'. No doubt, too, Littleton's series 'of the most eminent persons of my country' influenced West in his ideas for embellishing the hall at Alscot.

As an antiquary West was unusually concerned about likeness. Other eighteenth-century representations of Shakespeare seem to be derived from a single source (see comparative illustration); Rysbrack's bust was based on a combination of the two most authentic images of the bard, and in this it paralleled the trouble being taken at this date to establish a correct text for Shakespeare's plays. There is some evidence for the process of research. In 1758 Joseph Greene, the schoolmaster at Stratford, wrote to West about the taking of a plaster cast of the head from Gerard Johnson's monument of Shakespeare in Stratford Church for use as a model; Rysbrack also studied Kneller's copy of the Chandos portrait (National Portrait Gallery), although he said it had no 'Spirit in it'. Droeshout's engraving for the folio edition of Shakespeare's plays, 1632, seems to have moved him even less. Rysbrack has portrayed Shakespeare in early seventeenth-century dress, as in the Chandos portrait, with a hint of baroque swagger in the folds of his cloak; the bald head and the treatment of the hair are derived from Johnson's monument. The bust is very delicately carved, but, in spite of the care taken over the likeness, the head is stylized, the noble demeanour making Shakespeare seem more aristocratic in appearance than in reality he should have been.

Rysbrack's bill for the bust is dated 10 November 1759. In 1763 he was still in touch with West about the inscription on the pedestal. But West did not complete the decoration of the hall at Alscot (with a bust of Matthew Prior standing over the other fireplace, and another of Isaac Newton over the doorway) until 1763, hence his delay. Unaccountably, and inexcusably, West did not pay for the bust until after Rysbrack's death, on 6 March 1770.

Provenance: Commissioned by James West (*c.*1704–1772); by descent to James A.R. West; West sale, Christie's, 15 July 1986, lot 76, bt. Baskett and Day, from whom it was purchased.

Literature: M.J. Webb, *Michael Rysbrack, Sculptor*, 1954, pp. 117–20; NACF Review, 1988, pp. 124–5.

26

Admiral the Hon. John Byron (?)

Sir Joshua Reynolds (1723–1792)

Oil on canvas, 123.5 × 98 (48½ × 38½)
*c.*1748

City of Nottingham Museums, Newstead Abbey (NA 1026)

Sir Joshua Reynolds:
Admiral the Hon. John Byron
1759
Oil on canvas, 76 × 63.5 (30 × 25)
National Maritime Museum, Greenwich

This portrait, unknown to scholars until its sale at Sotheby's in 1978, is traditionally supposed to represent the Admiral Hon. John Byron (1723–1786), grandfather of the poet, an intrepid naval officer known as 'Foulweather Jack'. Mannings has argued that, since there is no allusion to the sea or to Byron's adventures, 1740–1746, after his shipwreck off the coast of Chile, indeed nothing to suggest that this is the portrait of a seafaring man, the picture is more likely to represent his eldest brother, William, 5th Lord Byron (1722–1798) of Newstead Abbey, Nottinghamshire. For the following reasons, however, the present writer is inclined to accept the traditional identification.

As Mannings points out, the work must, on stylistic grounds, have been painted before Reynolds's journey to Italy, 1749–1752. It belongs with that group of informal, freshly painted portraits, many of them of naval officers at Plymouth, which the young Reynolds painted between the end of 1746, when he returned from London to his native Devonshire at the time of his father's last illness, and May 1749, when he sailed from Plymouth with Captain Keppel, bound for Italy. Lord Byron would almost certainly have sat for his portrait in London, where, incidentally, his sister, Lady Carlisle, lived. Moreover, there is no particular reason for his patronizing Reynolds, even if the artist did return to the metropolis for short periods.

John Byron arrived at Dover from South America in March 1746, and remained in England until after the Peace of Aix-la-Chapelle, October 1748, when he captained a ship, part of a squadron led by Captain Buckle, off the coast of Guinea. On 8 September 1748 he married Sophia, daughter of John Trevanion, of Caerhays, Cornwall, later to be an intimate friend of Mrs Thrale and a favourite of Dr Johnson. Caerhays lies about half-way between St Austell and Falmouth, some thirty miles west of Plymouth, the centre of Reynolds's circle of patronage.

Reynolds certainly painted a portrait of Byron a decade later, in 1759, when he was a commodore (versions at Castle Howard, Yorkshire, and in the National Maritime Museum, Greenwich: see comparative illustration). Allowing for ten years or so difference in age the features in these portraits correspond closely enough with the physiognomy of the Newstead Abbey picture to confirm that the latter is a portrait of the same sitter.

If the Trevanion provenance for the picture is correct, it seems most likely that the portrait was painted for Byron's wife's family at the time of their engagement or marriage and before his renewed service abroad. This would explain, too, his portrayal as a fashionable young country squire rather than as a naval officer. Byron is wearing the kind of double-breasted frock coat and Kevenhuller hat popular in sporting circles at the time. The background, with its trees silhouetted against bright clouds, is characteristic of English portraiture in the late 1740s and 1750s.

Provenance: The Trevanion family, Caerhays, Cornwall, until *c.*1840; by descent to Sir Joseph Graves-Sawle; anon. sale, Sotheby's, 15 March 1978, lot 15, bt. for Newstead Abbey.

Literature: NACF Report, 1978, pp. 46–7; David Mannings in *Reynolds*, exh. cat., Royal Academy, 1986, no. 10.

27

The Revd Richard Canning

Thomas Gainsborough (1727–1788)

Oil on canvas, 76.2 × 63.5 (30 × 25)
c.1757

Ipswich Borough Museums and Galleries (R1958–136)

Richard Canning (1708–1775) was rector or vicar of several parishes in Suffolk, but notably of St Lawrence's, Ipswich, for just over forty years. He was also the editor of *The Suffolk Traveller*, 1764, a guide-book to the county written by Gainsborough's friend, Joshua Kirby. In about 1757 he and his friend, the Revd Henry Hubbard, both sat to Gainsborough for their portraits, which they exchanged with each other. A previously unknown portrait of this date of another member of this East Anglian clerical intelligentsia, the Revd Tobias Rustat, rector of Stutton near Ipswich, was recently acquired by Gainsborough's House, Sudbury.

After his training in London Gainsborough, modestly thinking of himself 'as one, among a crowd of young Artists, who might be able in a country town (by turning his hand to every kind of painting) to pick up a decent livelihood', returned to his native Suffolk to practise, first in Sudbury, then after 1752 in Ipswich. His clientèle was chiefly the local gentry and professional classes (lawyers, teachers and clergymen), and the bulk of his work head-and-shoulders portraits, which was what most people could afford, and for which he charged eight guineas. Gainsborough's ability to capture the presence of a sitter was remarkable even on this scale; his portrait of Canning is an especially good example of the elaborate system of hatching with which he was experimenting at this time, under the influence of the French pastellists La Tour and Perroneau, with the aim of giving more fullness to the flesh and a greater vitality of surface (see comparative illustration). Ramsay also imitated the pastellists' hatching technique, though in a softer way, in exactly these years. 'You please me much', Gainsborough wrote to a client in 1758, 'by saying that no other fault is found in your picture than the roughness of the surface ... being of use in giving force to the effect at a proper distance, and what a judge of painting knows an original from a copy by.'

Provenance: Given by the sitter to the Revd Henry Hubbard; by descent; London sale, 1955, bt. Michael Harvard; with Sidney Sabin, from whom it was purchased, 1958.

Literature: NACF Report, 1958, p. 21; Ellis Waterhouse, *Gainsborough*, 1958, no. 118a; John Hayes, 'Some Unknown Early Gainsborough Portraits', *Burlington Magazine*, vol. 107, February 1965, pp. 70 and 73.

Jean Baptiste Perroneau: *Portrait of a Man*
Oil on canvas, 51.5 × 40.6 (20½ × 16)
Private Collection

28

Robert Hay Drummond, Archbishop of York

Andrea Soldi (c.1703–1771)

Oil on canvas, 124.5 × 98.5 (49 × 38¾)
Signed and dated c.l.: *A.ᵈ Soldi Pinx.ᵗ /A.º 1755*

York City Art Gallery (1380)

Robert Hay Drummond (1711–1776) was the second son of Viscount Dupplin, later 7th Earl of Kinnoull, and grandson of Robert Harley, Earl of Oxford, Queen Anne's minister and a great bibliophile. Appointed a royal chaplain the year after his ordination, he became Archbishop of York at the age of fifty. Horace Walpole described him as 'a dignified and accomplished prelate'; genial and convivial as well as noble in manner, he was also a liberal patron of the arts. He sat to Reynolds in 1764 and to Hudson in about 1765. Drummond was Bishop of St Asaph at the time this portrait was painted.

Andrea Soldi, a Florentine, was one of those many foreign painters who came to England to seek their fortune in the years when the mainstream of British portraiture was at its most turgid, between the death of Kneller in 1723 and the rise of Reynolds (with a London studio) in 1753. He arrived in 1736, having been advised by British merchants in the Near East, whose portraits he had been painting, that he would do well in London. Between April and August 1738 he had 'above thirty portraits large and small begun', and, although Ramsay claimed to have put him to flight, he continued in good practice until the mid-1740s. Soldi was admired for his excellent draughtsmanship, his light, attractive colour, and his 'well immitated Silks Sattins Velvets'. The sound academic training he had received in Italy and his natural sense of design are evident in the firm modelling, assured placing of the hands and ample pyramidal structure of this accomplished portrait (contrast comparative illustration).

Provenance: Unrecorded until its appearance in anon. sale, Christie's, 20 November 1981, lot 119, bt. Colnaghi's, from whom it was purchased, 1983.

Literature: NACF Review, 1983, pp. 153–5.

Thomas Hudson: *Thomas Herring, Archbishop of Canterbury*
c. 1748
Oil on canvas, 127 × 101 (50 × 40)
The Master and Fellows of Corpus Christi College, Cambridge

29

The Revd Laurence Sterne

Sir Joshua Reynolds (1723–1792)

Oil on canvas, 127.3 × 100.4 (50⅛ × 39½)
Exhibited at the Society of Artists, 1761, no. 82
Signed and dated on one of the papers left: *J. Reynolds/pinx^t/1760*

National Portrait Gallery, London (5019)

Laurence Sterne (1713–1768) is chiefly renowned for his whimsical novel *The Life and Opinions of Tristram Shandy*, the first two volumes of which took London by storm when they were published there early in 1760. He was a celebrity when he arrived in the metropolis from Yorkshire in March. Reynolds arranged sittings with him immediately (20 March; 3, 6, 19 and 21 April); Thomas Gray refers to the picture on 22 April as 'now engraving', and Edward Fisher produced his fine mezzotint after the work in 1761. The portrait does not seem to have been commissioned, and Reynolds may never have sold it; it was probably still in his studio when it was re-exhibited at the Society of Artists in 1768, and the first recorded owner is his executor who, under the terms of Reynolds's will, was entitled to the picture of his choice. *Sterne* was the first portrait Reynolds exhibited under the sitter's name, and Kerslake has suggested convincingly that Reynolds painted the picture as a speculation; he had a close business relationship with his engravers, and would surely have had a share in Fisher's profits.

Penny describes the format of the picture as typical of Reynolds's early paintings of men of letters, comparing it with his portrait of Horace Walpole, 1757 (see comparative illustration), in which a hand is similarly held to the head and quill pen and appropriate papers (including a print he had commissioned of an antique marble eagle) are placed on the table beside him. The noble, pyramidal design, the broadly massed folds of the wide-sleeved black Geneva gown, and the strong highlighting of the head and hands, are all suggestive of the work of Titian, whom Reynolds revered. The expression is intense but subtle; a visitor to the Society of Artists exhibition in 1761 observed that Sterne appeared 'in as facetious a humour as if he would tell you a story of Tristram Shandy', the manuscript of which is on the table at his side.

Provenance: John Fitzpatrick, 2nd Earl of Upper Ossory (one of Reynolds's executors) by 1801; bequeathed in 1823 (or given previously) to his nephew, Henry Fox, 3rd Baron Holland; acquired from Lady Holland in 1840 (perhaps in exchange) by Henry, 3rd Marquess of Lansdowne; by descent to Katherine, Lady Nairne (Viscountess Mersey), from whom it was purchased through Agnew's, 1975.

Literature: Algernon Graves and William Vine Cronin, *A History of the Works of Sir Joshua Reynolds P.R.A.*, 1899–1901, vol. 3, pp. 933–5; NACF Report, 1975, pp. 12–13; John Kerslake, *Early Georgian Portraits*, National Portrait Gallery, 1977, vol. 1, pp. 260–3; Nicholas Penny in *Reynolds*, exh. cat., Royal Academy, 1986, no. 37.

Sir Joshua Reynolds: *The Hon. Horace Walpole*
1757
Oil on canvas, 127 × 101.6 (50 × 40)
The Marquess of Hertford, Ragley Hall, Warwickshire

Laurence Sterne.

30

The Revd Laurence Sterne

Joseph Nollekens (1737–1823)

Marble, 39.4 (15½) high
*c.*1766 (or later)

National Portrait Gallery, London (1891)

Sterne left London for the Continent in 1762, and lived for two years in southern France. His second sojourn abroad, 1765–1766, bore fruit in his *A Sentimental Journey through France and Italy*, 1768. Nollekens was working in Rome as a young man, 1760–1770, and his original terracotta bust of Sterne must have been made when the writer was in the city, either in January or in March-April 1766.

Nollekens was the son of an Antwerp painter who settled in London in 1733 and studied with Scheemakers before going to Italy; he sculpted most of the eminent men of his age, and was one of the finest of all British portrait sculptors. His first portrait bust was one of David Garrick, done in Rome in 1764, the success of which led Sterne to agree to sit. The realistic though sensitively ennobled characterization (which makes the Reynolds seem generalized), the formula for modelling the hair in loose curls, and the bare neck and shoulders, all testify to Nollekens's study of late Roman portrait sculpture. In his later portrait of Charles James Fox, of which, like his *William Pitt*, there are innumerable versions, he used a Roman toga draped across the shoulders with splendid baroque swagger. Nollekens made several marble busts from his terracotta of Sterne (all, including the Gallery's bust, probably executed after his return from Italy in 1770), of which there are examples at the Laurence Sterne Trust (Shandy Hall, Coxwold) and in the Henry E. Huntington Art Gallery (San Marino, California). He always regarded this youthful work as one of his best, and he is shown leaning upon it in the portrait Rigaud made of him (see comparative illustration).

Provenance: Nollekens sale, Christie's, 3–5 July 1823, 2nd day, lot 79*, bt. Palmer; Mrs Russell sale, Christie's, 17–18 March 1847, 2nd day, lot 421, bt. Graves; Francis Broderip; Broderip sale, Christie's, 6 February et seq. 1872, 2nd day, lot 266, bt. Heugh; with Amor, from whom it was bought by G.B. Croft-Lyons, who presented it, through the NACF, 1920.

Literature: NACF Report, 1920, p. 31; John Kerslake, *Early Georgian Portraits*, National Portrait Gallery, 1977, vol. 1, pp. 265–7.

John Francis Rigaud:
Joseph Nollekens the Sculptor with the bust of Laurence Sterne
1772
Oil on canvas, 76.2 × 63.5 (30 × 25)
Yale Center for British Art, Paul Mellon Collection

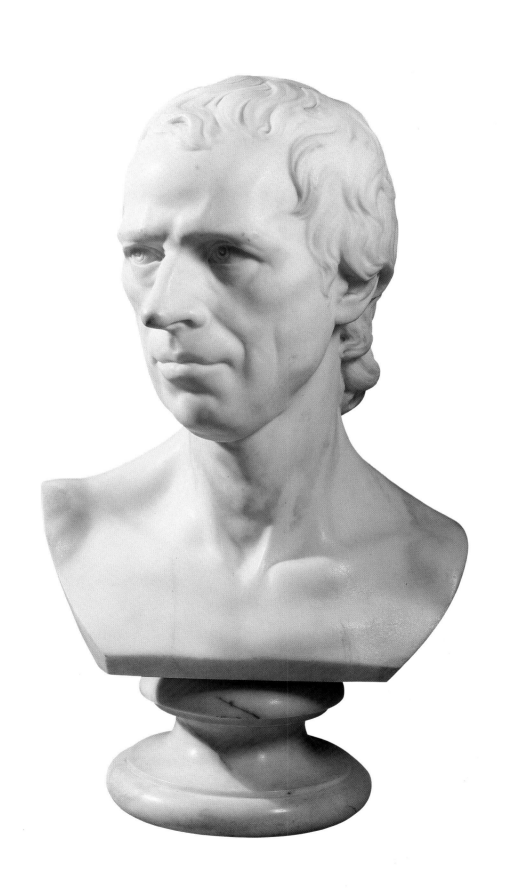

31

David Garrick in 'The Provok'd Wife'

Johan Zoffany (1733–1810)

Oil on canvas, 99 × 124.5 (39 × 49)
1763–5. Exhibited at the Society of Artists, 1765, no. 167

Wolverhampton Art Gallery & Museums (607)

William Hogarth: *A Scene from 'The Beggar's Opera'*
c. 1729–1731
Oil on canvas, 56.6 × 76.3 (22½ × 29¾)
Tate Gallery, London

David Garrick (1717–1779), who left Lichfield for London at the age of twenty in the company of Dr Johnson, established himself on the London stage with a triumphant performance as Richard III at Goodman's Fields Theatre in 1741. He was then engaged for Drury Lane, the theatre which he managed from 1747 until his retirement in 1776. One of the greatest actors of all time, 'a master both in tragedy and comedy' (Johnson), he dominated the theatre in Britain for thirty years, engaging the best possible talent and revolutionizing methods of staging and performance: among his reforms the declamatory style of acting was replaced by natural speech, spectators were banished from the stage, and stage lighting was concealed from the audience. A close friend of Reynolds and Gainsborough, Garrick was immensely vain and was painted several times by both artists as well as by numerous others.

Garrick became the first important English patron of Zoffany, after the latter's arrival in this country from Germany in 1760, commissioning from him four conversation pieces of himself, his family and his friends in the garden of his villa on the banks of the Thames at Hampton. Zoffany's fresh naturalism and meticulous attention to detail (which cost him dear in effort and time spent) soon brought him success in the country which loved Canaletto. He was taken up by Queen Charlotte, who in 1772 commissioned his celebrated masterpiece *The Tribuna of the Uffizi* (Royal Collection). After six years in Italy and a cool reception for his *Tribuna* Zoffany found he had lost his practice in London, and in 1783 he resorted to a sojourn in Bengal, where he remained until 1789.

Among Zoffany's early works for Garrick were several scenes showing the great actor in his favourite roles, which Zoffany exhibited at the Society of Artists to further his reputation, and Garrick had engraved to enhance his. The genre was one which had been initiated by Hogarth in the earlier years of the century (see comparative illustration). In this scene Garrick is playing Sir John Brute in Vanbrugh's comedy *The Provok'd Wife*. In the course of a drunken evening frolic with Lord Rake and Colonel Bully, Sir John robs a journeyman tailor of clothes intended for his own wife and, exclaiming that he is Queen Boudicca, prepares to resist arrest by the watch. In this farcical scene Garrick was able to make full use of the expressively mobile features for which he was renowned. The watchmen, with their varied and vividly portrayed reactions, are all likenesses of the actors who appeared in the cast at Drury Lane on the night of 18 April 1763 (Henry Vaughan, Hullet, Thomas Clough, William Parsons, Thomas Phillips and Watkins), and the scene may be accepted as true to the action in that production. A study which Zoffany made for the central figure of Garrick himself (Shakespeare Memorial National Theatre Trust, Stratford-upon-Avon) is said to have been altered at the sitter's request. The picture seems to have taken about two years to complete; when it was returned from exhibition at the Society of Artists in the summer of 1765, Garrick hung it in his dining parlour at Hampton. It was engraved by John Finlayson, 1 November 1768.

Provenance: Painted for David Garrick; by descent to Mrs Trevor; Mrs Trevor sale, Sotheby's, 19 July 1972, lot 28; anon. sale, Sotheby Parke-Bernet, New York, 6 March 1975, lot 97; Roy Miles, from whom it was purchased, 1976.

Literature: Geoffrey Ashton and Iain Mackintosh in *The Georgian Playhouse*, exh. cat., Arts Council, 1975, no. 27; NACF Report, 1976, pp. 42–3; Mary Webster in *Johan Zoffany 1733–1810*, exh. cat., National Portrait Gallery, 1976, no. 18.

32

Mrs Thomas Riddell

Sir Joshua Reynolds (1723–1792)

Oil on canvas, 239 × 148.5 (94⅛ × 58⅜)
*c.*1763

Laing Art Gallery, Newcastle upon Tyne
(Tyne and Wear Museums)

Elizabeth (1730–1798), only daughter and heiress of Edward Horsley Widdrington, of Felton Park, Northumberland, married Thomas Riddell, of Swinburne Castle, Northumberland, in 1760. No sitting is recorded in Reynolds's sitter-books, so she probably sat in 1763 (the year for which Reynolds's sitter-book is missing). A payment of 100 guineas is recorded in the artist's ledger, 18 November 1766.

Reynolds was very conscious of Gainsborough's move towards a more naturalistic style in his full-length portraits of the 1760s and, always competitive, took up some of his designs and motifs and endeavoured to surpass them. The concept of the sitter walking gently into the landscape, which may, however, have been his own invention, is comparable with Gainsborough's *The Byam Family* (see comparative illustration). In both artists' work, the trees are integral both to design and effect; here they play a vital role in the suggestion of movement across the canvas. In contrast to the stagey trees (Mrs Riddell is not walking in a real landscape, let alone a garden), the distant water and fields beyond are naturalistic in conception. Pale and delicate in colour, and unusually thin in handling, this tender image is far removed from the intentions of Reynolds's 'grand manner' portraits, and it is significant that it was neither exhibited nor engraved. It is a very private painting of a recently married woman, rather plain in looks and pensive in expression.

Provenance: By descent to J.C. Riddell, from whom it was purchased, 1965.

Literature: Algernon Graves and William Vine Cronin, *A History of the Works of Sir Joshua Reynolds P.R.A.*, 1899–1901, vol. 2, p. 824; NACF Report, 1965, p. 15; David Mannings in *Reynolds*, exh. cat., Royal Academy, 1986, no. 51.

Thomas Gainsborough:
Mr and Mrs George Byam and their eldest daughter Selina
c. 1764
Oil on canvas, 249 × 238.8 (98 × 94)
Marlborough College, Wiltshire

33

Lady Stanhope and Lady Effingham as Diana and her Companion

Francis Cotes (1726–1770)

Oil on canvas, 281 × 183 (110⅝ × 72)
Signed and dated c.r.: *F Cotes* [the FC in monogram] *px*.*. 1765*

York City Art Gallery (1414)

Sir Joshua Reynolds:
Anne Delaval, Lady Stanhope
1765
Oil on canvas, 236.2 × 146 (93 × 57½)
The Baltimore Museum of Art, The Mary Frick Jacobs Collection
(BMA 1938.77)

Anne Hussey Delaval (1736–1812), one of the eleven children of Francis Blake Delaval, was the third wife of Sir William Stanhope, forty years her senior, from whom she separated in 1763. She was evidently an amateur artist, to judge by the many accessories included in the full-length portrait Reynolds painted of her in 1765 (see comparative illustration). Anne's younger friend, Catherine Proctor (1746–1791), a daughter of Metcalfe Proctor, of Thorpe, near Leeds, married Thomas, 3rd Earl of Effingham, in 1765.

Francis Cotes was trained as a pastellist by George Knapton, and most of his work was in this medium until the end of the 1750s. In 1763 he acquired a handsome studio in Cavendish Square, and the demand for his portraits in oils was soon as great as for those of Reynolds and Gainsborough; his prices – twenty, forty and eighty guineas – were half-way between those charged by the two better-known artists. Sir Ellis Waterhouse explained his popular success: 'He went all out for health and youth and fine clothes, a strong likeness and no nonsense. His complexions are usually of milk and roses, his men bear no burden of intellect and his ladies are neither bold nor pensive; his draperies … look as if they had come out of a bandbox.'

Lady Stanhope, identifiable as Diana the huntress from her hair ornament in the form of a crescent moon, is seen here commanding her attendant, Lady Effingham, to unleash her hound to give chase to the stag in the distance. This double portrait of the two young ladies dressed in wrapping gowns is the most ambitious of Cotes's female full-length portraits of the late 1760s, in which he abandoned the loveliness of contemporary costume for the nondescript classical drapery and mythological imagery employed by Reynolds for his grand exhibition pictures. However, whereas Reynolds was concerned with generalizing his forms and idealizing his sitters, conferring upon them the attributes of goddesses, Cotes retained his fundamental interest in physical appearance, that is to say, in likeness, decorative detail and elaborate drapery folds with a life of their own.

Waterhouse was surely correct in believing that this double portrait was related to the private theatricals staged by Lady Stanhope's and Lady Mexborough's brother, Sir Francis Blake Delaval, rather than to Reynolds's elevated concept of universal values. Mead Johnson's impression was that 'these women are not goddesses, but very pretty human beings who are having a marvellous time, dressed up in the latest fashion for grand portraiture, while they act out their roles in a play'. The picture was Cotes's unintellectual answer to Reynolds's *Lady Sarah Bunbury sacrificing to the Graces*, attended by Lady Susan Fox Strangways (Fig. 15), exhibited at the Society of Artists in 1765. Lady Stanhope's slightly empty expression and the sweeping elongated arc of her posture, perhaps influenced by Reynolds's celebrated portrait of the Duchess of Hamilton as Venus (Lady Lever Art Gallery, Port Sunlight), exhibited at the Society of Artists in 1760, may be compared with the sobriety and elegant classical contrapposto of Reynolds's portrayal of the same sitter a few years earlier.

One of the most remarkable features of Cotes's painting is the elaborate and finely carved rococo frame, ably discussed by Green. 'It bears', he writes, 'an armillary sphere with trumpets top centre, plumed helmets, halberds and swords at the sides and a pistol, cannon barrel and sword at the bottom. The sphere is a symbol of the universe whilst all the other features are emblems

of war. Such a frame might be expected on a portrait of a great military leader, but what, might well be asked, is it to do with either of the sitters in the York picture or their assumed roles?' Five other frames are known to have been commissioned in the same pattern. Three were at Methley Hall, Yorkshire, the seat of Lord Mexborough, and two remain at Doddington Hall, Lincolnshire, the house of Lord Mexborough's brother-in-law, Sir Francis Blake Delaval. Sir Francis was a military hero of the Seven Years War and Green advances the hypothesis that his engraved portrait by Reynolds, now in an unrelated frame, may have been the starting point for the series of martial frames.

Provenance: Passed from Lady Stanhope to her sister, Lady Mexborough; thence by descent to John, 8th Earl of Mexborough; purchased, 1987.

Literature: Edward Mead Johnson, *Francis Cotes*, Oxford, 1976, pp. 30–1 and 92; Richard Green,'"The Hon. Lady Stanhope and the Countess of Effingham as Diana and her Companion" by Francis Cotes', NACF Review, 1988, pp. 106–9.

34

Mrs Henry Verelst

George Romney (1734–1802)

Oil on canvas, 235 × 144 (96 × 56)
*c.*1771–1772

Clifton Park Museum, Rotherham Metropolitan Borough Council
(OP.2/87)

Ann Wordsworth (1751–1835), daughter of Josiah Wordsworth, of Wadsworth Hall, near Doncaster, married Henry Verelst (died 1785), of Aston Hall, Rotherham, in 1771, the year after his return from India, where he had served as Governor of Bengal, 1767–1770.

Romney came to London from his native Kendal in 1763, and developed a style based on the graceful, flowing line of classical drapery, which he studied in the Duke of Richmond's sculpture gallery, open to artists. He travelled to Italy to study the art of classical antiquity at first hand, 1773–1775, and on his return to London took a lease on Cotes's former studio in Cavendish Square. Unsociable, introspective and obsessed by ideal art – historical and mythological compositions for which he produced hundreds of drawings but little finished work – Romney was nonetheless a hard-working society portraitist, who achieved success through the pursuit of the same neutral qualities of looks and breeding that had absorbed Cotes. Although his prices were always lower than those of Reynolds and Gainsborough, he was recognized as their only rival. It was in keeping with his nervous character, but very unusual amongst aspiring and established portrait painters alike, that he never submitted his painting to the public gaze of the annual Royal Academy exhibitions.

The portrait of Mrs Verelst, an uncluttered and beautifully harmonious design, which thrives on such anatomical impossibilities as the length of the left thigh, is one of the finest examples of Romney's style immediately preceding his visit to Italy. The maturity of Romney's transformation into contemporary terms of what he had learnt from classical art, even before he had had a sight of Rome, is substantiated by the graceful turn of the head, the elegant curving contour of the right side, the felicitous disposition of the folds in the wrapping gown emphasized by the dignified motion down the steps, the refined colour, and the broad, generalized features making up the background. As Robinson has pointed out, the source which Romney used for the portrait was the Mattei *Ceres* (see comparative illustration), well known in England from reproductions, and of which a cast was owned by the Royal Academy.

Provenance: By descent to H.S. Verelst; Verelst Settlement sale, Christie's, 21 June 1974, lot 97, bt. Grieg; anon. sale, Sotheby's, 21 November 1984, lot 46, bt. Colnaghi's, from whom it was purchased.

Literature: John Martin Robinson in *The British Face*, exh. cat., Colnaghi's, 1986, no. 33; NACF Review, 1987, pp. 162–3.

Unknown artist: The Mattei *Ceres*
3rd century BC, or a later Hellenistic work
Marble, height 106.5 (42)
Vatican Museums, Rome

35

The Bradshaw Family

Johan Zoffany (1733–1810)

Oil on canvas, 132.3 × 175.6 (52 × 69)
Exhibited at the Society of Artists, 1769, no. 359,
as 'A gentleman's family'.

Tate Gallery (6261)

Johan Zoffany: *John, Duke of Atholl and his Family*
1765–1767
Oil on canvas, 93.5 × 158 (36¾ × 62¼)
The Duke of Atholl, Blair Castle, Tayside

Horace Walpole identified this group in a note he made in his Society of Artists exhibition catalogue: 'Mr Bradshaw Secretary of the Treasury'. Thomas Bradshaw (1733–1774), seen here resplendently attired in a scarlet and gold waistcoat, had a distinguished official career, ending up as a Lord of the Admiralty in 1774. In that year he shot himself because of financial worries. He married in 1757 Elizabeth Wilson (died 1802); they had seven children, of whom one, Thomas, died young, and two, Augustus and Charlotte, were born after this picture was painted. Mrs Bradshaw is seen towards the right of the canvas; the other lady has been identified as Bradshaw's sister. The four children are presumably, from left to right, Barrington (1761–1804), Elizabeth (1767–1793), Lawrence (1768–1853) and Robert (1759–1835), the eldest son.

Zoffany is perhaps best known today for his conversation pieces. His earliest essays in this genre were the four delightful pictures he painted in the early 1760s, soon after coming to England, of Garrick, his family and his friends in the gardens of Garrick's villa at Hampton. Both these and his equally fine group of the Atholl Family (Blair Atholl), done in the mid-1760s, are fairly loosely constructed, although the figures in the latter are unified by means of an intricate series of connecting diagonals (see comparative illustration). In *The Bradshaw Family*, although four of the heads, echoing the slope of the oak tree trunk, are placed in a similar, very contrived, diagonal, the arrangement is pyramidal, with Thomas Bradshaw as the apex, a compositional formula favoured by Zoffany. Each member of the family is animated by some form of domestic or recreational activity, with the boy on the left detached from the rest, absorbed in flying a kite (the string of which forms a diagonal line echoing those on the right). X-radiographs show that Mrs Bradshaw's head was at first turned three-quarters to the left. As in most of Zoffany's conversation pieces, the figures are arranged in two closely-linked planes, near the foreground, as on a stage, a procedure which gives them equal importance in the canvas. The costume is meticulously painted, in the tradition of contemporary German portraiture; and the background is neatly divided into a middleground (separated from the foreground by a clump of plants) and a distance composed of naturalistically rendered, enclosed fields.

The Bradshaw Family, which, as Milner writes, 'presents that Georgian ideal of family life which was exemplified in the Royal Family', was exhibited in the same year, 1769, that Reynolds exhibited *Lady Blake as Juno* and other of his canvases overtly imitating the Old Masters. Zoffany's world was at the opposite end of the artistic spectrum from the idealized generalizations of Reynolds; but both satisfied different aspirations of eighteenth-century British society.

Provenance: Robert Haldane Bradshaw (the boy on the right of the picture); by descent to Thomas B. Bradshaw; anon. (= C.H.Y. Bradshaw) sale, Christie's, 20 June 1930, lot 112, bt. Gooden & Fox for Ernest E. Cook, who bequeathed it (with the rest of his collection) to the NACF; allocated, 1955.

Literature: NACF Report, 1955, p.34–5; Martin Davies, *The British School*, National Gallery Catalogues, 2nd edn, 1959, pp. 112–13; Barbara Milner in *A Gift to the Nation: The Fine and Decorative Art Collections of Ernest E. Cook*, exh. cat., Holburne Museum and Crafts Study Centre, Bath 1991, no. 41.

36

Charles Towneley's Library in Park Street, London

Johan Zoffany (1733–1810)

Oil on canvas, 127 × 99 (50 × 39)
1781–1783

Towneley Hall Art Gallery and Museums,
Burnley Borough Council (PA/OIL 120)

Charles Towneley (1737–1805), a fastidious bachelor collector, seen on the right with his dog Kam, is seated among his finest pieces of sculpture in the library of his London home, No. 7 Park Street (now Queen Anne's Gate: house demolished) – what the *Public Advertiser* in 1785 called 'the Wilton House of London'. Opposite him is the French antiquary, Pierre Hugues, better known as d'Hancarville (?1729–1805), a sponger whom Towneley had invited to catalogue his collection; he sits next to the collector's most prized object, the bust of Isis (or Clytie), which was the basis for d'Hancarville's theory about the origin of Greek art in Egypt. Behind stands Charles Greville (1749–1809), then the lover of Emily Hart (later Emma Hamilton), who is expounding on Isis to the antiquary Thomas Astle (1735–1803). The Towneley Venus, discovered at Ostia in 1775, dominates the background; Clytie, recut in the eighteenth century, has that gentle, contemplative expression so modish in the age of *sensibilité*. The sculptures are as animate as the group of connoisseurs. The Towneley Hall Art Gallery, in which Zoffany's portrait now hangs, was until 1902 the family home of the Towneley family.

Zoffany's meticulously naturalistic paintings give the impression of being accurate records of a particular scene. In fact he habitually transposed objects in order to strengthen his concept or improve a composition (see comparative illustration). Towneley's library is no exception. There was no space either in this room, or any other in the house, to accommodate so many sculptures, and J.T. Smith, who as a student had been employed by Towneley to make drawings for him, wrote of the painting that 'it was a portrait of the Library, though not strictly correct as to its contents, since all the best marbles displayed in various parts of the house were brought into the painting by the artist, who made it up into a picturesque composition according to his own taste'. An account of the marbles and the places from whence they came (MS., Towneley Hall) was compiled 'According to Mr. Zoffany's desire'. The *Discobolus*, in the left foreground, found at Hadrian's Villa at Tivoli and wrongly restored (the head, which does not belong, should have been turned to watch the discus), was added to the picture in 1792, at Towneley's request.

Towneley's collection, like those of Henry Blundell, Lord Shelburne and William Weddell, reflected the neo-classical taste of the 1760s. It had been built up largely during his stay in Italy, 1765–1772, with the help of the neo-classical painter, Gavin Hamilton, who was also an excavator and a dealer (it was whilst in Italy that Towneley met Zoffany, who became a close friend). The collection was sold to the British Museum, of which Towneley had been a Trustee, after his death, and was housed in a special gallery, the Towneley Gallery. It was only after the arrival in London of the Elgin marbles that it was realized, as the sculptor John Flaxman informed the House of Commons Committee appointed to decide whether the Parthenon sculptures should be purchased for the nation, that 'the greater part of Mr Towneley's Marbles, with some few exceptions, are perhaps copies, or only acknowledged inferior works' by Roman sculptors of the first and second centuries AD. The collection is still, however, housed in its own gallery at the Museum (Room 84).

Provenance: Given by the artist to Charles Towneley; by descent to Maurice Towneley, 3rd Lord O'Hagan; O'Hagan sale, Christie's, 19 May 1939, lot 92, bt. Vicars Gallery for Burnley Corporation.

Literature: NACF Report, 1939, p. 22; Mary Webster, 'Zoffany's painting of Charles Towneley's Library in Park Street', *Burlington Magazine*, vol. 106, July 1964, pp. 316–28; Ronald Paulson, *Emblem and Expression: Meaning in English Art of the Eighteenth Century*, 1975, pp. 152–3; Mary Webster in *Johan Zoffany 1733–1810*, exh. cat., National Portrait Gallery, 1976, no. 95; Francis Russell in *The Treasure Houses of Britain*, exh. cat., National Gallery of Art, Washington, D.C., 1985, no. 213.

Johan Zoffany: *Sir Laurence Dundas with his Grandson*
1769–1770
Oil on canvas, 101.5 × 127 (40 × 50)
Private Collection

37

Sir Joseph Banks

Sir Joshua Reynolds (1723–1792)

Oil on canvas, 127 × 101.5 (50 × 40)
Exhibited at the Royal Academy, 1773, no. 239

National Portrait Gallery, London (5686)

Benjamin West: *Sir Joseph Banks*
c. 1771
Oil on canvas, 234 × 160 (92 × 63)
Lincolnshire County Council Recreational
Services: Usher Gallery, Lincoln
In West's portrait Banks is shown wearing a Maori
cloak; a Tahitian head-dress is seen in the background.
Most of the objects collected on the voyage still survive
in the collections of the Museum of Mankind and the
National History Museum.

Sir Joseph Banks (1743–1820), an autocratic President of the Royal Society for over forty years, 1778–1820, inherited a large fortune when he came of age which he spent lavishly on his botanical and scientific interests. In 1766 he travelled to Newfoundland to collect plants with Constantine Phipps (later Lord Mulgrave), Gainsborough's naval friend. Two years later he accompanied Captain Cook's famous three-year voyage round the world in the *Endeavour*, 1768–1771, travelling at his own expense with the botanist, David Solander, later to be his librarian, two draughtsmen and assistants; New Zealand and Australia were discovered on this voyage, and Banks brought home valuable ethnographical and natural history collections (see comparative illustration). On his return from the South Seas he became George III's chief scientific adviser, and persuaded the king to turn the gardens of his palace at Kew into a centre for cultivating exotic botanical specimens. A patron rather than a writer himself, his house and extensive library were open to any scientist, and he bequeathed his collections and books to the British Museum.

Banks sat to Reynolds (now President of the Royal Academy and at the height of his powers) in 1772, before and after his last voyage, to Iceland. Reynolds habitually attended the meetings of the Royal Society, and was a frequent visitor to Banks and his companion, Solander, at the British Museum, where their collections were arranged. He was a great admirer of the explorer, and his portrait, completed in 1773 and immediately engraved by W. Dickinson, suggests Banks's immense energy and determination. Seated by a globe, with his clenched hand resting on a letter bearing the inscription from an ode by Horace – *Cras Ingens interabimus aequor* ('Tomorrow we'll sail the vasty deep again') – Banks is shown ready for fresh adventures. As Leslie and Taylor wrote, 'The burning eyes are focussed by the will that knits the brow, and . . . The energy of the man seems to be lifting him out of his seat by an irrepressible force'. The power and resonance of the image stems not only from the shared sympathies of artist and sitter but from Reynolds's ability to select a characteristic and expressive pose and to exclude unnecessary detail from the picture. As so often, his central idea was borrowed from the Old Masters. Shawe-Taylor has pointed out that the motif of showing Banks half-rising derives from the principal figure in Rembrandt's great masterpiece, *The Syndics* (see comparative illustration).

Provenance: By descent from the sitter through the Brabourne family to the Hon. Mrs Clive Pearson; the Hon. Clive Gibson, from whom it was purchased, through Agnew's, 1986.

Literature: Charles Robert Leslie and Tom Taylor, *Life and Times of Sir Joshua Reynolds*, 1865, vol. I, pp. 427–9; Algernon Graves and William Vine Cronin, *A History of the Works of Sir Joshua Reynolds P.R.A.*, 1899–1901, vol. I, p. 47; NACF Review, 1987, p. 131; Desmond Shawe-Taylor, *The Georgians: Eighteenth-Century Portraiture & Society*, 1990, pp. 93–4.

Rembrandt van Rijn:
The Syndics (The Sampling Officials of the Drapers' Guild)
1662
Oil on canvas, 190 × 280.8 (74 × 109½)
Rijksmuseum, Amsterdam

38

Dr James Hutton

Sir Henry Raeburn (1756–1823)

Oil on canvas, 125.1 × 104.8 (49½ × 41¼)
c.1783

Scottish National Portrait Gallery, Edinburgh (PG 1556)

James Hutton (1726–1797), with his varied accomplishments, was a true son of the Scottish Enlightenment; an exhibition of Raeburn portraits of Hutton and his friends was held at Edinburgh University in 1976. Trained as a doctor in Paris and Leiden as well as in Edinburgh, Hutton then studied agriculture in Norfolk and farmed in Berwick, spending the later years of his life as a geologist: in his *Theory of the Earth*, 1795, he originated the modern theory of the formation of the earth's crust. Hutton was also joint editor of Adam Smith's *Essays on Philosophical Subjects* (1795).

Raeburn, who settled in Edinburgh New Town as a portraitist in 1786, was the first portrait painter of any distinction deliberately to seek his career in Edinburgh. Genial and popular, with a breadth of interests both learned and sporting, he became the undisputed leader of his profession in that city after the death of David Martin in 1797, and dominated the artistic scene in Scotland for over a quarter of a century. Largely self-taught, Raeburn (like Reynolds) painted straightaway onto the canvas without preliminary drawings, using a personal technique involving square, flat touches – a bold, direct style well suited to the independent, innovative society he portrayed with such assurance.

Raeburn's portrait of Hutton is an early work, executed before his travels abroad, 1784–1786, and before he had formed his idiosyncratic personal style; thus inevitably it shows certain awkwardnesses, for example, in the positioning of the left knob of the chair and the treatment of the left leg, and, most obviously, in the set, immobile expression of the head. But the finely painted still life of books and geological specimens, the informality of the loosened waistcoat, the feeling for substance in the head and hands, and the concentrated light which was later to become an effective formula for strengthening modelling, are already characteristic of the mature Raeburn (see comparative illustration).

Provenance: Mr Davidson of Streatfield: Sir George Warrender, Bt.; Lady Bruntisfield; Bruntisfield sale, Christie's, 18 April 1986, lot 129B.

Literature: NACF Review, 1986, p.141.

Sir Henry Raeburn: *Sir John Sinclair*
1810–1813 (?)
Oil on canvas, 123.2 × 98.4 (48½ × 38¾)
National Portrait Gallery, London

39

Captain William Wade

Thomas Gainsborough (1727–1788)

Oil on canvas, 234.3 × 153 (95½ × 60½)
Exhibited at the Royal Academy, 1771, no. 78

Victoria Art Gallery, Bath City Council (BATVG P 1988.1)

William Wade (died 1809) was an illegitimate son of Field Marshal Wade, the commander-in-chief who failed to stop Prince Charles Edward's march south in 1745, and MP for Bath, 1722–1748. Partly owing to his good looks, which attracted the female voters and earned him the title of the 'Bath Adonis', he was elected Master of Ceremonies at Bath in 1769; he held this post successfully for eight years until in 1777 he was cited for adultery, giving rise to the witticism that he had 'waded out of his depth', and was obliged to quit Bath.

Gainsborough settled in Bath in 1759, having exhausted the limited patronage available to him around Ipswich. He achieved a quick success with the fashionable clientèle that thronged the spa town during the season, began to paint on a larger scale than hitherto, and exhibited regularly at the Society of Artists' exhibitions in London, of which the first was held in 1760, and then at the Royal Academy, of which he was a founder member, 1768.

In order not to detract from his characterizations, and because he disliked formal trappings, Gainsborough normally set his full-length portraits against landscape backgrounds, which were often used to complement the design (see comparative illustration). His portrait of Captain Wade in all his finery, vain and disdainful, was no exception, and thus it was exhibited at the Royal Academy. As a result of the criticism, however, that a wholly rural setting – 'as though he intended to bow/To an ox or an ass – to a heifer or a cow' – was inappropriate for the sophisticated Master of Ceremonies, Gainsborough painted in a balustrade and flight of steps down from the suggestion of a grand country mansion: the original clouds and trees can be seen under the increasingly transparent paint. (Both the steps and a bush lower right have disappeared during cleaning, before the picture was acquired by Bath.) The affected pose was based on a painting then attributed to Van Dyck with which Gainsborough would have been familiar at Wilton House, the full-length of James Stuart, Duke of Lennox. Shawe-Taylor has commented that 'Wade's upright carriage, extended foot and hand on hip suggest an orchestra waiting to strike up a minuet'. The low viewpoint reflected the position for which the canvas was designed to be hung.

The picture, a splendid advertisement for the artist (who presented it to the proprietors), was finally placed in the Octagon Card-Room of the New Assembly Rooms (where it once again hangs) and Gainsborough was given three complimentary tickets to the Ridotto to celebrate the opening on 30 November 1771.

Provenance: Given by the artist to the Proprietors of the New Assembly Rooms, Bath; their sale, Christie's, 18 July 1903, lot 141a, bt. Lane for Michael Bass, 1st Baron Burton; offered in partial lieu of tax by the Burton Trustees, and acquired, 1988.

Literature: Ellis Waterhouse, *Gainsborough*, 1958, no. 697; Ann Sumner in *Gainsborough in Bath*, exh. cat., Holburne of Menstrie Museum, Bath, 1988, no. 20; Sam Hunt, 'Captain Wade Returns to Bath', NACF Review, 1989, pp. 113–14; Desmond Shawe-Taylor, *The Georgians: Eighteenth-Century Portraiture & Society*, 1990, pp. 65–9.

Thomas Gainsborough: *General James Johnston*
c. 1763–1764
Oil on canvas, 206 × 141 (18¼ × 55½)
National Gallery of Ireland, Dublin
The curvilinear rhythm of the general's scarlet coat is taken up in the silver birch behind.

40

George Drummond

Thomas Gainsborough (1727–1788)

Oil on canvas, 233 × 151 (90 × 58)
c.1779–1782

The Visitors of the Ashmolean Museum, Oxford (A878)

George Drummond (1758–1789), of Stanmore, the second son of Robert Hay Drummond, Archbishop of York (see no. 28), was a senior partner in Drummond's Bank. He married as his second wife Martha, the eldest daughter and co-heiress of Thomas Harley, a wealthy banker and government contractor who had been Lord Mayor of London in 1767. The wedding took place on 30 November 1779, about a year after Henry Holland had started to build Berrington Hall, Herefordshire (now National Trust), for Harley. Austere on the exterior, with grounds by Capability Brown, the house is lavishly decorated inside, and the full-length portraits of George and Martha Drummond (see comparative illustration) which Harley commissioned from Gainsborough at the time of, or soon after, their marriage must have formed part of the decorative scheme.

Eighteen months after the Drummond marriage, on 10 April 1781, Harley's second daughter, Anne, married Lord Rodney's eldest son, George. Harley then commissioned from Gainsborough (since 1774 established in London) three-quarter-length portraits of both his daughters, intimate likenesses in identical blue silk dresses, to hang at Berrington. He also asked Gainsborough to paint a full-length of Lord Rodney, and acquired from Thomas Luny and Richard Paton four battle pieces representing Rodney's exploits against the French and Spanish fleets, 1780–1782. Gainsborough's portraits were all sold in the 1880s by the 7th Lord Rodney; the battle pieces, and other portraits, remain in the house.

Gainsborough painted George Drummond in his customary manner for a full-length portrait, elegantly dressed but posed in a generalized rural setting. The sitter is shown leaning against an outcrop of grassy rock similar to a plinth, with the oak tree on the right arching over him in an opposite direction. The low viewpoint and downward gaze suggest that the picture was destined for a particular, and fairly high, position. Mrs Drummond is similarly treated, but is leaning against the base of a column and looking directly out at the spectator. Both portraits are excellent examples of Gainsborough's loose and assured proto-romantic style of the 1780s.

Provenance: Commissioned by Thomas Harley; by descent to George, 7th Baron Rodney, who sold it c.1887 to Michael Bass, 1st Baron Burton; Baroness Burton sale, Christie's, 4 May 1951, lot 46, bt. Gooden & Fox for Ernest E. Cook, who bequeathed it (with the rest of his collection) to the NACF; allocated, 1955.

Literature: NACF Report, 1955, p. 29; Ellis Waterhouse, *Gainsborough*, 1958, no. 210.

Thomas Gainsborough: *Mrs George Drummond*
c. 1779–1782
Oil on canvas, 228.6 × 147.3 (90 × 58)
Montreal Museum of Fine Arts

41

The Morning Walk

Thomas Gainsborough (1727–1788)

Oil on canvas, 236 × 179 (93 × 70½)
1785

The Trustees of the National Gallery, London (6209)

William Hallett (1764–1842), of Canons, Edgware, son of the distinguished cabinet-maker of the same name, and Elizabeth Stephen (1763/4–1833), of Brakespear, were married on 30 July 1785. Gainsborough painted this marriage portrait, as much a hymn to the romance of young love as it is a likeness of the two individuals, in the autumn of that year. He was paid 120 guineas for the picture, his usual price at this time for a full-length including a horse, in March 1786.

Bate Dudley in the *Morning Herald* described the portrait of the Halletts as 'in nouvelle stile'; and indeed it was. In the mid 1780s Gainsborough was developing the art of portraiture – in line with his popular 'fancy' pictures of sentimental subjects, the first of which he exhibited at the Royal Academy in 1781 – in the direction of a distillation of poetic mood. In this he was closer to the spirit of the romantic age than his vastly more influential rival, Reynolds. *The Morning Walk* (a title for the portrait of the Halletts which is of nineteenth-century origin) is the most sophisticated example of a type of composition in which the sitter is seen walking gently forward towards the spectator, in a landscape that is not just a setting but of which he or she (generally she) forms an indissoluble part (see comparative illustration). Mrs Hallett's costume, with its apple-green ribbons and bows, diaphanous wrap and sketchiness of handling, almost melts into the softly painted foliage of a sylvan landscape as arcadian as anything in Watteau (with whom Gainsborough was at this period compared). In spite of the lively Spitz dog, superbly painted, which strikes a note of domestic realism, the nineteenth-century French poet, Théophile Gautier, said that, in front of this picture, he felt 'a strange retrospective sensation, so intense is the illusion it produces of the spirit of the eighteenth century. We really fancy we see the young couple walking arm in arm along the garden avenue'. The contrast in mood and impressionistic handling with the fresh naturalism of *Mr and Mrs Robert Andrews* (no. 21) is complete.

Provenance: Apparently inherited by the Halletts' daughter, Lettice Elizabeth (1787–1859), who married Nash Crosier Hilliard; offered for sale at Foster's, 9 August 1834; exhibited for sale at John Allnutt's Pall Mall Gallery; W.E. Hilliard (grandson of the sitters) by 1859; bought from the Hilliard collection in 1884 by Agnew's, who sold it to Sir Nathan (later Lord) Rothschild; thence by descent to Victor, 3rd Baron Rothschild, from whom it was purchased, 1954.

Literature: NACF Report, 1954, pp. 12, 15; Ellis Waterhouse, *Gainsborough*, 1958, no. 335; Martin Davies, *The British School*, National Gallery catalogue, 2nd edn., 1959, pp. 44–5; John Hayes in *Thomas Gainsborough*, exh. cat., Tate Gallery, 1980–1981, no. 130; Desmond Shawe-Taylor, *The Georgians: Eighteenth-Century Portraiture & Society*, 1990, pp. 131–2.

Thomas Gainsborough: *Sophia Charlotte, Lady Sheffield*
1785
Oil on canvas, 223.7 × 148.7 (89½ × 59½)
The National Trust, Waddesdon Manor, Buckinghamshire

42

The Revd d'Ewes Coke with his Wife and Daniel Parker Coke

Joseph Wright of Derby (1734–1797)

Oil on canvas, 152.4 × 177.8 (60 × 70)
*c.*1780–1782

Derby Art Gallery (676–1965)

The Revd d'Ewes Coke (1747–1811), in the centre, rector of Pinxton and South Normanton, Derbyshire, who had been orphaned at the age of eleven, inherited his guardian's house, Brookhill, near Pinxton, in 1780. He probably commissioned Wright's group portrait soon after he came into possession of the house. The artist's receipt for the payment of seventy-two guineas is dated January 1783. Coke's wife, Hannah, was the daughter and heiress of George Heywood, of Brimington Hall, Derbyshire. Daniel Parker Coke (1745–1825), a distant cousin, was elected MP for Derby in 1776, but in 1780 was returned for Nottingham, a city he represented for thirty-three years. At about the time of this portrait Daniel Coke bought two views of Cromford from Wright, one of them depicting Richard Arkwright's newly erected cotton mills ablaze with light during the night shift.

Wright, trained in the 1750s under Hudson, was one of those exceptional eighteenth-century painters who decided to make his career in the provinces, and without the benefit of aristocratic patronage. His originality as an artist stemmed from this decision, and from the attitudes of mind of the local circles in which he moved: the self-made men who created the Industrial Revolution in the Midlands, and the middle-class patrons of his native Derbyshire, for whom realism was paramount and the accepted conventions of painting in London meant little. Although he made his name with his extraordinary candlelight pictures and industrial scenes, the bulk of his work was in the usual genre, portraiture. Sir Ellis Waterhouse rightly described the d'Ewes Coke picture as Wright's 'masterpiece of group portraiture'.

The three Cokes, almost certainly portrayed in the grounds of Brookhill, are grouped round a rough garden table in a broadly triangular pattern of which d'Ewes is the apex, their attention focused on the distant landscape. Hannah Coke is holding a portfolio of her drawings and pointing to one held by Daniel; both of them are comparing it with the real view beyond. D'Ewes is pointing to the view and, with his left arm round his wife's shoulder, seems to be complimenting her on her drawing. The suggestion made in the NACF Report that the picture illustrates a discussion on the subject of the planning of the garden seems a less plausible interpretation, as the object of their gaze is not close at hand. The postures and expressions, and the treatment of the various objects introduced, are naturalistic and convincing; Hannah's green dress turns to yellow as the sun catches it. Everything is in its place and everything is in harmony (see also comparative illustration).

Provenance: By descent in the family to R.G.S. Coke, from whom it was purchased in 1965.

Literature: NACF Report, 1966, p. 17; Benedict Nicolson, *Joseph Wright of Derby: Painter of Light*, 1968, vol. I, pp. 72–3, 96, 124–5 and 188–9; Judy Egerton in *Wright of Derby*, exh. cat., Tate Gallery, Grand Palais, Paris, and Metropolitan Museum of Art, New York, 1990, no. 142.

Joseph Wright of Derby:
The Reverend Thomas Gisborne and his Wife Mary
1786
Oil on canvas, 185.5 × 152.5 (73 × 60)
Yale Center for British Art, Paul Mellon Collection

43

The Wood Children

Joseph Wright of Derby (1734–1797)

Oil on canvas, 167.7 × 134.7 (66 × 53)
Signed and dated b.l.: *I.W.P./1789*

Derby Art Gallery (499–1934)

The young sitters are Robert, John and Mary, children of Hugh and Sarah Wood, of Swanwick, Derbyshire, of whom Wright painted head-and-shoulders portraits at the same time. Wright described the group in his account book as 'A conversation'. His price was eighty guineas.

The three children are grouped in the front plane of the canvas, and are framed by trees and foliage. Robert, who, somewhat surprisingly, is knocking in stumps with his cricket bat (a bat of the curved variety used by cricketers at that time), is distracted by the cricket ball his sister has thrown into the air. Mary's head is bathed in light, and both are gazing up at the ball in wonderment, faintly echoing the children absorbed by the orrery in Wright's famous candlelight picture of that subject (Derby Art Gallery). Although Nicolson prefers the slightly earlier group of the Leaper children for its 'spontaneity and charm' (see comparative illustration), Wright's pictures are nearly always still, their action, movement and inter-relationships frozen for the artist's painstaking record.

Provenance: By descent to R.H. Wood; Wood sale, Christie's, 1 June 1934, lot 62, withdrawn and sold to the NACF, from whom it was acquired.

Literature: NACF Report, 1934, p. 36; Benedict Nicolson, *Joseph Wright of Derby: Painter of Light*, 1968, vol. I, pp. 71 and 226–7.

Joseph Wright of Derby: *The Leaper Children*
c. 1785
Oil on canvas, 172.7 × 137.2 (68 × 54)
Private Collection

44

The Ladies Waldegrave

Sir Joshua Reynolds (1723–1792)

Oil on canvas, 143.5 × 168 (56½ × 66)
1780–1781. Exhibited at the Royal Academy, 1781, no. 187, as
'Portraits of three ladies'

National Galleries of Scotland, Edinburgh (NG 2171)

Sir Joshua Reynolds: *Three Ladies Adorning a Term of Hymen*
1773–1774
Oil on canvas, 233.6 × 291 (92 × 114½)
Tate Gallery, London

Sir John Everett Millais: *Hearts are Trumps*, 1872
Oil on canvas, 165.7 × 219.7 (65¼ × 86½)
Tate Gallery, London

The painting represents three daughters of James, 2nd Earl
Waldegrave, and Maria Walpole (later Duchess of Gloucester),
illegitimate daughter of Sir Edward Walpole, Horace Walpole's
brother. They are, from left to right, Lady Charlotte Maria
(1761–1808), Lady Elizabeth Laura (1760–1816) and Lady Anna
Horatia (1762–1801). The sittings took place in May and June
1780, with final appointments in March 1781, when the picture
was being prepared for exhibition. The receipt for payment of 300
guineas is dated 7 June 1782.

When he saw it at the Royal Academy Walpole described the
picture as 'a most beautiful composition; the portraits very like,
and the attitudes natural and easy'. After he had had it at home
for a couple of years – it was hung on a pale blue wall in the
refectory at Strawberry Hill – Walpole was more critical; as he
told William Mason (10 February 1783), 'though the effect of the
whole is charming, the details are slovenly, the faces only red and
white; and his [Reynolds's] journeyman, as if to distinguish
himself, has finished the lock and key of the table like a Dutch
flower-painter'.

In his celebrated portrait of the three Montgomery sisters
adorning a Term of Hymen (exhibited Royal Academy, 1774; see
comparative illustration), Reynolds adopted poses taken from the
Old Masters and used that nondescript classicizing kind of
costume which he hoped would give a sense of timelessness to his
'grand manner' portraiture. The Waldegrave group retains in the
background the column on a high parapet and swathe of deep red
curtain which historically were part of the trappings of an
'important' portrait, and had nothing to do with the walls of an
actual room, such as Zoffany would have painted. Otherwise the
picture is a charming and intimate conversation piece, with Maria
holding a skein of silk, Laura winding it, and Horatia, demurely
posed, working at her tambour; the three young women are
united pictorially, by their industry and by sisterly affection. It is
true that the dresses are broadly handled, but in this Reynolds
was helped by fashion, which, as Aileen Ribeiro has noted,
'was moving towards a kind of simplicity which, if not strictly
classical, was far less dominated by trimmings and patterned
textiles ... He has depicted the Waldegrave sisters in white
muslin, *the* fashionable textile of the decade'. As Shawe-Taylor has
pointed out, the picture is an image of becoming female modesty,
expressive of the age of *sensibilité*. Reynolds had a wide range of
styles and invention at his command, and the ability to succeed
in each. A fine mezzotint of Horace Walpole's picture of his 'three
fair nieces' was published by Valentine Green, 1 December 1781.
The late Victorians, imitating the eighteenth century, gave their
inventions a slightly hothouse glamour (see comparative illustration).

Provenance: Commissioned by Horace Walpole, great-uncle of the sitters,
who inscribed their names on the back of the stretcher; bequeathed to
Anne Damer, his executrix and residuary legatee; inherited with the
other contents of Strawberry Hill by John, 6th Earl Waldegrave, 1815;
George, 7th Earl Waldegrave, Strawberry Hill sale, Robins, 18 May 1842,
lot 35, bt. in; by descent to his widow's fourth husband, Chichester, Baron
Carlingford; with Agnew's, who sold it to Daniel Thwaites, 1886; by
descent to his grandson, Robert, 1st Baron Alvingham, from whom it was
purchased, 1952.

Literature: Algernon Graves and William Vine Cronin, *A History of the Works
of Sir Joshua Reynolds P.R.A.*, 1899–1901, vol. 3, pp. 1017–19; Violet
Biddulph, *The Three Ladies Waldegrave*, 1938, pp. 155–7; NACF Report, 1952,
p. 16; David Mannings in *Reynolds*, exh. cat., Royal Academy, 1986, no. 122;
Desmond Shawe-Taylor, *The Georgians: Eighteenth-Century Portraiture &
Society*, 1990, p. 117.

45

Wilson and Jane Gale-Braddyll and their Son

Sir Joshua Reynolds (1723–1792)

Oil on canvas, 238.1 × 147.3 (93¾ × 58)
1789

The Syndics of the Fitzwilliam Museum, Cambridge
(PD.10–1955)

Wilson Gale-Braddyll (1756–1818), of Conishead Priory,
Lancashire, MP for Lancaster 1780–1784, married Jane Gale in
1776; their son, Thomas, was born in the same year. In 1784
Reynolds exhibited a full-length portrait of young Thomas, then
aged seven, and in 1788 painted head-and-shoulders portraits of
Mr and Mrs Gale-Braddyll, of which the former was shown at the
Academy that year. The additional sitting for the family group
took place in 1789. According to Henry Bate-Dudley, writing in
the *Morning Herald* for 30 May 1789, the figure of Mrs Braddyll
was introduced after the picture had been started. Gale-Braddyll,
a wealthy landowner, entertained both the Prince of Wales and
the Duke of York at Conishead in the year this portrait was
painted.

As in many of Reynolds's last works the figures are somewhat
elongated, a tendency emphasized by the narrowness of the
canvas, which is the size normally used for a single full-length.
The perspective of the bench on which Mrs Braddyll is sitting,
and the foreshortening of the rim of the sculptured urn, are
misunderstood, and Mrs Braddyll's right hand is awkwardly
painted: Reynolds was never an assured draughtsman. The dog,
too, is unconvincing. But the colouring is fresh, and the handling
of Mrs Braddyll's skirt impressionistic. One contemporary critic
wrote that 'about Mrs. B.'s hands and drapery there are some
parts not finished'. The studied informality of the group may be
contrasted with Wright of Derby's more down-to-earth treatment
in his portrait of the Arkwright family (see comparative
illustration).

The picture must have been one of the last Reynolds painted
before he lost the sight of his left eye, and gradually gave up
work. Against the names of his sitters for 13 July 1789 he
scrawled in his sitter-book: 'prevented by my Eye beginning to
be obscured'.

Provenance: Lt-Col. Thomas Richmond-Gale-Braddyll (the boy in the
portrait); anon. (=Braddyll) sale, Christie's, 23 May 1846, lot 44, bt.
Bishop; W.J. Isbell, of Stonehouse; T. Pooly Smyth, of Plymouth, by 1857;
anon. (=Pooly Smyth) sale, Christie's, 13 June 1859, lot 213, bt. in; Revd
C.W. Randolph; Lionel, 2nd Baron Rothschild, Tring Park, by 1899; by
descent to Victor, 3rd Baron Rothschild, who gave it to the Lord Baldwin
Fund for Refugees for sale at Christie's, 24/25 May 1939, 2nd day, lot 256,
bt. Gooden & Fox for Ernest E. Cook, who bequeathed it (with the rest of
his collection) to the NACF; allocated, 1955.

Literature: Algernon Graves and William Vine Cronin, *A History of the Works
of Sir Joshua Reynolds P.R.A.*, 1899–1901, vol. I, pp. 111–12; NACF Report,
1955, p. 24; J.W. Goodison, *Catalogue of Paintings*, vol. III, British School,
Fitzwilliam Museum, Cambridge, 1977, pp. 204–5; Barbara Milner in *A Gift
to the Nation: The Fine and Decorative Art Collections of Ernest E. Cook*, exh. cat.,
Holburne Museum and Crafts Study Centre, Bath, 1991, no. 28.

Joseph Wright of Derby:
Richard Arkwright and his Wife Mary and Child
1790
Oil on canvas, 243.8 × 158.7 (96 × 62½)
Private Collection

46

Henry, 1st Baron Brougham and Vaux

Sir Thomas Lawrence (1769–1830)

Oil on panel, 114.1 × 82 (45 × 32¼)
1825

National Portrait Gallery, London (3136)

Henry Brougham (1778–1868), though intellectually vain, often superficial, unreliable and of an irritable disposition, was a brilliant and tireless advocate. His defence of Queen Caroline at her trial in the House of Lords, 1820, brought him immense popularity. An energetic administrator and reformer, he helped to set up mechanics' institutes in collaboration with his fellow Scot, George Birkbeck, who founded the University of London, 1828, and, as Lord Chancellor, instituted the central criminal court. He gave his name to an unusually shaped carriage, custom-built for him by Robinson, the coachmaker.

Lawrence was a boy wonder, renowned by the age of ten for his profile portrait drawings. He established his reputation with two magnificent full-lengths shown at the Royal Academy in 1790 – *Queen Charlotte* (National Gallery) and *Elizabeth Farren* (Metropolitan Museum of Art, New York) – and by the age of twenty-five had succeeded Reynolds as Painter-in-Ordinary to the King and been elected a full Academician. Distinguished by his romantic outlook and glittering technique, he no longer had rivals after the death of Hoppner in 1810 and commanded huge fees. He became the President of the Royal Academy in 1820. The Regency age was also the age of Lawrence.

Lawrence painted Brougham shortly after the latter's election as Rector of Glasgow University. According to two letters the artist wrote to the engraver, William Walker (National Portrait Gallery Archive), the work was commissioned by Walker for the purpose of engraving, and painted between July and September 1825. Walker had a cast made of Brougham's face to ensure accuracy. In the course of the work Lawrence enlarged the portrait from a three-quarter length to the present 'unusual dimensions', though without making any additional charge. Walker did not produce his mezzotint until November 1830, after which he sold the picture to Raeburn's son.

In spite of the increasing demands made on him after his triumph with the magnificent series of paintings of the allied sovereigns and war leaders victorious against Napoleon (see comparative illustration), Lawrence was at the height of his powers during the last decade of his life, and his portrait of Brougham, fluent, sparkling and vivacious, is successfully evocative not only of the lawyer's dynamism but also of his wit and humour.

Provenance: Commissioned by the engraver, William Walker; sold by him to Henry Raeburn, Jr., *c.*1830; said to have been bought at Christie's in 1858 by Henry, 5th Duke of Newcastle; by descent to Henry, Earl of Lincoln (later 9th Duke of Newcastle); Lincoln sale, Christie's, 31 March 1939, lot 29, bt. Fine Art Society, from whom it was purchased, 1943.

Literature: NACF Report, 1943, p. 17; Richard Walker, *Regency Portraits*, National Portrait Gallery, 1985, vol. 1, p. 66; Kenneth Garlick, *Sir Thomas Lawrence: A complete catalogue of the oil paintings*, Oxford, 1989, no. 134.

Sir Thomas Lawrence: *The Archduke Charles of Austria*
1819
Oil on canvas, 269.9 × 178.4 (106¼ × 70¼)
Royal Collection, Windsor Castle
(by gracious permission of Her Majesty The Queen)

47

Priscilla Jones

Thomas Barker (1769–1847)

Oil on canvas, 76.2 × 63.5 (30 × 25)
*c.*1793?

The Holburne Museum and Crafts Study Centre, Bath (A 341)

Priscilla Jones married Thomas Barker in 1803. The exact date of her portrait has not been established, but it is traditionally supposed to be a companion to Barker's self-portrait, painted after his return from Italy in 1793 (see comparative illustration).

Barker was a youthful prodigy who was encouraged, and practically adopted, by Charles Spackman, a wealthy Bath coach-builder. An artist of extraordinary facility, he copied landscapes by the Old Masters, and copied and imitated the landscapes and fancy pictures of Gainsborough, who had worked in Bath for fifteen years. After three years in Rome, for which Spackman paid, and a short time in London, Barker spent the rest of his life in Bath, painting landscapes and rustic scenes in an eclectic style.

This enchanting portrait of his bride-to-be in a smart yellow bonnet is undoubtedly one of his masterpieces. The smooth, almost enamelled, modelling is quite unlike British portraiture of the period, and suggests the influence of Continental neo-classical painters whom he would have encountered in Rome.
The sculptural folds of the cloak, the huge Doric columns and the antique statue in the niche in the background all enhance the foreign-looking appearance of the canvas. In the companion portrait Barker has on his easel a view of the Great Cascade and the Temple of the Sibyl at Tivoli.

Provenance: By descent in the Barker family to G.S. Hobson, from whom it was acquired by the NACF, and presented, 1939.

Literature: NACF Report, 1939, p. 30; Mary Holbrook, 'Painters in Bath in the Eighteenth Century', *Apollo*, vol. 98, November 1973, p. 381; *The Barkers of Bath*, exh. cat., Victoria Art Gallery, Bath, 1986, no. 16.

Thomas Barker: *Portrait of the Artist*
c. 1793
Oil on canvas, 79.4 × 64 (31¼ × 25¼)
The Holburne Museum and Crafts Study Centre, Bath

48

Thomas Gibbs Hilton with his Hound 'Glory'

Ben Marshall (1767–1835)

Oil on canvas, 91 × 70.9 (35⅞ × 27⅞)
Signed and dated b. l.: *B. Marshall pt./1822*

Royal Museum & Art Gallery, Canterbury (CANCM 10344)

Thomas Hilton (1750–1826), known as 'Glory' Hilton from his devotion to his favourite hound of that name, was one of the most celebrated fox-hunting sportsmen of his day, and especially revered in his home county of Kent. His reputation was at its height during the hey-day of Sir Edward Knatchbull's Provender Hunt; after the dispersal of the Provender pack, he kept his own pack of hounds at Selling.

Ben Marshall, who settled in Newmarket in 1812, is best known for his naturalistic and anatomically striking characterizations of the greatest racehorses of the day (see comparative illustration), but he also made equally realistic studies of jockeys and stable lads. He worked for the *Sporting Magazine* regularly from 1796 onwards, and the portrait of Hilton was probably a commission from that magazine, which published an engraving of it by William Smith to accompany an article on Hilton in its issue for August 1822. The house in the background of the picture is not Hilton's seat, Marshes, at Selling, but Lees Court, the seat of the Earl of Sondes. Marshall's portrayal both of Hilton and his hound, indistinguishable in importance, is direct, down-to-earth and unsqueamish. As always, Marshall emphasizes the bone structure of the animal.

By this time sporting activity, condemned for most of the eighteenth-century as barbarous, rowdy and prone to excesses of all kinds, had become associated with the nostalgia for English rural life, and both the sporting community and sporting art came into their own during the Revolutionary and Napoleonic Wars (1793–1815). As Stephen Deuchar has written, there was then 'a rekindled admiration for the old seventeenth-century-based sporting ideal, one which argued country sportsmen's robust physical health, warlike capabilities, hospitality, national loyality and personal generosity.' Hilton, in his seventies, so wrote the *Sporting Magazine*, 'mounts and dismounts with the agility of youth, was never known out of spirits, or had the headache – for which blessing he thanks the health-enlivening chase'.

Provenance: By descent in the family to the sitter's great-great-granddaughters, from whom it was acquired, 1983.

Literature: The Sporting Magazine, vol. 10, August 1822, p. 217; Aubrey Noakes, *Ben Marshall*, Leigh-on-Sea, 1978, no. 166; NACF Review, 1984, p. 154.

Ben Marshall: *Sam with Sam Chifney Jnr. Up*
1818
Oil on canvas, 101.6 × 127 (40 × 50)
Henry E. Huntington Library and Art Gallery, San Marino, California
Sam Chifney won the 1818 Derby on Sam.

49

The Duke of Atholl's Keeper, John Crerar, with his Pony

Sir Edwin Landseer (1802–1873)

Oil on board, 59 × 43 (23¼ × 16⅞)
Inscribed and dated on label on verso: *Four sketches by Landseer/ painted at Blair Atholl in 1824/Keeper John Crerar with pony*

Perth Museum and Art Gallery (FA 19/78)

John Crerar (died 1843) entered the service of the dukes of Atholl in 1776, and became an accomplished musician as well as a skilled deer-stalker. By the date of this sketch he was Head Keeper at Blair Atholl, and a legendary figure in the sporting world of his day; there are references to him in William Scrope's *The Art of Deer Stalking*, first published in 1839 with illustrations by Landseer.

Landseer, an infant prodigy, achieved instant professional success as a specialist in animal and sporting painting and was a full Academician before he was thirty. He became the most popular painter of his day and the favourite of Queen Victoria. A sharp observer of what he saw, with a capacity for fluent sketching in oils as well as in pen and ink, he tended, especially in his later years, to romanticize his compositions, idealizing domestic as well as untamed animals. His best-known image is still *The Monarch of the Glen*.

Landseer first visited Scotland in the autumn of 1824, and his study of John Crerar was one of a number of brilliant oil sketches he made in connection with a commission from the Duke of Atholl for a large picture of the death of a hart in Glen Tilt (see comparative illustration). Crerar is shown scanning the distant hills with an eager eye, his spyglass under his arm.

Provenance: C. Porter by 1830; Collin Young; anon. (= Vokins) sale, Christie's, 17 March 1877, lot 95, bt. in; R.W. Smith; Smith sale, Christie's, 6 February 1880, lot 61; anon. sale, Christie's, 17 May 1945, lot 68, bt. Bernard; with Scott and Fowles, New York, by 1951; anon. sale, Sotheby Parke-Bernet, New York, 10 November 1975, lot 376; anon. sale, Sotheby's, Gleneagles Hotel, 28–9 August 1978, 2nd day, lot 583, bt. Perth Art Gallery.

Literature: NACF Report, 1978, p. 29.

Sir Edwin Landseer: *Death of a Hart in Glen Tilt*
1824–1830
Oil on canvas, 149.8 × 208.8 (59 × 79)
The Duke of Atholl, Blair Castle, Tayside

50

Sir John Everett Millais, Bt.

George Frederic Watts (1817–1904)

Oil on canvas, 64.8 × 52.1 (25½ × 20½)
Exhibited at the Royal Academy, 1871, no. 172

National Portrait Gallery, London (3552)

George Frederic Watts: *John Stuart Mill*
1873
Oil on canvas, 66 × 53.3 (26 × 21)
National Portrait Gallery, London

John Everett Millais (1829–1896), Rossetti and Holman Hunt were the founders in 1848 of the Pre-Raphaelite Brotherhood, a movement that crystallized the growing taste for pre-High Renaissance art, represented by the Campo Santo frescoes in Pisa, and rejected the emptiness of contemporary academic painting. The brethren embarked on a programme of working directly and patiently from nature, using an accumulation of minutely observed detail and bright, decorative Quattrocento colour. Millais was the only natural painter of the three, and for ten years he produced a series of pictures executed on Pre-Raphaelite principles that are among the glories of British painting. By 1871, however, when Watts produced this portrait, he had sacrificed principles to Mammon, and was concentrating his energies on commissioned portraits, popular history paintings, fancy pictures and sentimental genre. Ruskin had once thought Millais the natural successor to Turner.

In 1885 Millais was created a baronet. That same year Watts refused a similar honour; he refused it again nine years later. Watts was a visionary. Inspired by the sight of Michelangelo's Sistine Ceiling, he resolved to paint a series of frescoes illustrating the history of mankind which he called *The House of Life*. The scheme came to nothing (for one thing large-scale mural painting required assistants, and he had none), but over the years much of his energy was devoted to allegorical easel paintings which revolved round this concept. In the field of portraiture – for which he was more highly regarded in his lifetime (as he is today) – Watts had similarly lofty notions. He conceived the idea of a 'Hall of Fame', a galaxy of heroic portraits, profoundly characterized, of the most distinguished men and women of his age, the sitters to be chosen by himself. Watts believed that 'the character of a nation as a people of great deeds is one that should never be lost sight of'; and his intention was to present his portraits to the Nation. Since the National Portrait Gallery (founded in 1856) was precluded by the rules laid down by its trustees from acquiring portraits of living sitters, this natural destination could not be the repository, but fifteen of his portraits were acceptable to the Gallery in 1895 and others were bequeathed by Watts at his death, those representing living persons remaining in the Watts Gallery for later transfer. Over fifty are now in the Gallery's possession; part of the series is displayed in London and part in the Gallery's Victorian outstation at Bodelwyddan Castle, Clwyd.

Watts's portrait of Millais – focused on the head like the rest of the series – is in energetic profile, and, although the critic of the *Athenaeum* (1871) thought it was painted on an off day, it perfectly suggests the robust vitality of the prolific society painter. There was nothing spiritual about Millais to support the reaction of Josephine Butler to her own portrait: 'It is rather terrible. It bears the marks of storms and conflicts and sorrows so strongly ... He said he wanted to make me looking into Eternity ... I don't think my friends will like it. But then he is not doing it for us, but for posterity; and no doubt it will convey an idea of my hard life work.' Watts's portrait of John Stuart Mill is perhaps the noblest and most searching of the whole series (see comparative illustration).

Provenance: By descent from the sitter to his grandson, Sir Ralph Millais, Bt., from whom it was purchased, 1948.

Literature: NACF Report, 1948, p. 20.

51

Effie Millais (Mrs John, later Lady, Millais)

Sir John Everett Millais, Bt. (1829–1896)

Oil on canvas, 99.6 × 84.1 (39 × 33)
1873

Perth Museum and Art Gallery

Euphemia Chalmers Gray (1828–1893), daughter of George Gray, a Writer to the Signet in Edinburgh, married John Ruskin, whose parents were old friends of her father, and whom she had known since she was a child, in 1848. The marriage was not a success, and was dissolved in 1854; the following year she married Millais, who had fallen in love with her during that fateful visit to Glenfinlas in Scotland in 1853, when Ruskin had taught him to paint rocks and water, the natural forces that most inspired Turner, as essential associative elements in any portrait of himself (see comparative illustration).

Millais retained an overriding concern for factual detail all his life, and devoted most of his later career to society portraiture – prosaic, often sentimental, sometimes powerful – which earned him great wealth and a baronetcy. His portrait of his wife, who had borne him eight children, and was then in her mid-forties, is a characteristic example of his easy realism and accomplished technique. There are overtones of Venetian sixteenth-century painting in the rich, wine-coloured velvet dress. According to Spielmann, the artist originally painted his youngest son, John Guille, sitting on his mother's lap, but scraped him out and replaced him with a matter-of-fact accessory in the shape of a copy of the *Cornhill* magazine.

Provenance: By descent to Sir Ralph Millais, Bt.; Millais sale, Christie's, 7 July 1967, lot 116, bt. Ferrers Gallery for Sir David Ross; Ross sale, Christie's, 24 January 1975, lot 79 (withdrawn); sold by his executors, 1977.

Literature: M.H. Spielmann, *Millais and his Works*, Edinburgh and London, 1898, p. 156; NACF Report, 1977, p. 104.

Sir John Everett Millais: *John Ruskin*
1853–1854
Oil on canvas, 78.7 × 68 (31 × 26¾)
Private Collection

52

Monna Vanna (Alexa Wilding)

Dante Gabriel Rossetti (1828–1882)

Oil on canvas, 88.9 × 86.4 (35 × 34)
Signed in monogram and dated b.r.: *DGR 1866*

Tate Gallery (3054)

Alexa Wilding was an aspiring actress whom Rossetti encountered in the Strand one evening in 1865 and persuaded to sit for him. Her 'beautiful face and golden auburn hair' conformed so closely to Rossetti's conception of ideal beauty that she became his most regular model at this time; he even paid her a retaining fee so that she would not pose for anyone else.

Rossetti, son of an Italian political refugee who became Professor of Italian at King's College, London, was equally distinguished as a passionately romantic painter and poet, and as a translator of Dante. Becoming firm friends with Holman Hunt through his admiration of the latter's *Eve of St Agnes*, he was, with Hunt and Millais, one of the three founders of the Pre-Raphaelite Brotherhood. Rossetti's painting, however, was inspired by a love of poetry, and an obsession with a particular type of female beauty that seemed to express his very soul; possessed of an ardent imagination, Rossetti had no interest in nature, no taste for the microscopic analysis that excited his comrades, and, barely competent in the rudiments of his profession, never cared whether his pictures were in perspective or not. The mistress whom he eventually married, Elizabeth (Lizzie) Siddal, Beatrice to his Dante, was the wan, frail and consumptive model for a series of portrait drawings, some of which are amongst Rossetti's most beautiful works. After her suicide in 1862, he resorted to a variety of models for his idealized portrait compositions before, later in that decade, falling irretrievably (and impossibly) in love with William Morris's wife, Jane, the subject from then on of all his most powerful painting.

Rossetti originally entitled this portrait of Alexa Wilding *Venus Veneta*. He wrote in September 1866, 'I have a picture close on completion – one of my best I believe, and probably the most effective as a room decoration which I have ever painted. It is called "Venus Veneta", and represents a Venetian lady in a rich dress of white and gold – in short the Venetian ideal of female beauty.' The picture is indeed sumptuously Venetian, with the head encircled by majestic drapery forms, though, as Grieve notes, the great sleeve actually recalls Raphael's portrait of Joan of Aragon (Louvre, Paris) or, perhaps more relevantly, his *La Donna Velata* (Palazzo Pitti, Florence). As in most of Rossetti's work, the figure fills the picture space and depth, which the artist found difficult to handle, is avoided; the white and gold drapery, spiral pearl clasp and red coral necklace are familiar accessories. The face itself is cold and expressionless; as Rossetti's studio assistant wrote, Alexa Wilding lacked 'variety of expression. She sat like the Sphynx waiting to be questioned and with always a vague reply in return; about the last girl one would think to

have the makings of an actress in her'. She may have had the full, sensuous lips that Rossetti found so appealing in women, and there may have been some physical resemblance between her and Jane Morris (though, as Holman Hunt wrote, Rossetti altered features to accord with his ideal), but she did not begin to possess the mysterious yet earthy qualities that drew him to Jane. Hilton called the painting 'icily aloof'. By contrast, Rossetti's great portrait of Jane as *Astarte Syriaca* (the Syrian Aphrodite) (see comparative illustration) is massive and brooding, a Wagnerian goddess rather than a Venetian courtesan, anything but 'effective . . . room decoration' (see comparative illustration). The title *Monna Vanna*, from Dante's *La Vita Nuova*, which Rossetti had translated, was given to the portrait of Alexa after the work was finished. Rossetti retouched the picture at Kelmscott in 1873 and renamed it 'Belcolore'.

Provenance: W. Blackmore, who sold it to George Rae, Birkenhead, 1869; acquired, 1916.

Literature: NACF Report, 1916, p. 25; Timothy Hilton, *The Pre-Raphaelites*, 1970, p. 186; Virginia Surtees, *Dante Gabriel Rossetti 1828–1882: The Paintings and Drawings: A Catalogue Raisonné*, Oxford, 1971, vol. 1, no. 191; Andrea Rose, *Pre-Raphaelite Portraits*, Oxford, 1981, p. 109; Alastair Grieve in *The Pre-Raphaelites*, exh. cat., Tate Gallery, 1984, no. 136.

Dante Gabriel Rossetti: *Astarte Syriaca*
1875–1877
Oil on canvas, 182.9 × 106.7 (72 × 42)
Manchester City Art Gallery

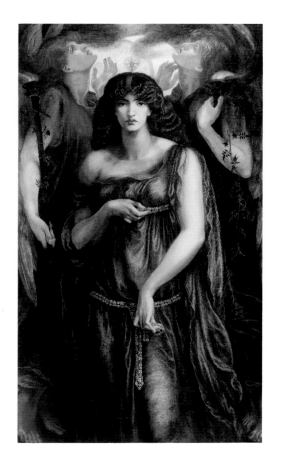

53

Charles Ricketts

Charles Shannon (1863–1937)

Oil on canvas, 95.3 × 99.1 (37½ × 39)
Signed and dated b.l.: *M·D·CCC·XC·VIII*

National Portrait Gallery, London (3106)

Charles Ricketts (1866–1931), a leading member of the 'aesthetic' movement, founder of the Vale Press and rival of Beardsley, was a polymath of his day: wood-engraver, book-illustrator, printer and editor; painter, stage designer, art critic and collector; and a brilliant conversationalist with a wide circle of artistic and literary friends, though 'one had to be on one's rarest behaviour – for nothing ordinary is expected'. He met Shannon at the time of his apprenticeship to the wood-engraver Roberts at the City and Guilds Technical Art School; the two youngsters were soon sharing lodgings, and they continued to live together, collaborating on every enterprise, for the rest of their lives (see comparative illustration). Their friend Sturge Moore wrote that 'between Ricketts and Shannon existed the most marvellous human relationship that has ever come within my observation, and in their prime each was the others complement, but neither easily indulged the other; their union was more bracing than comfortable'. Both lived for art, but Ricketts was the natural leader and the more significant of the two men; amongst his prolific output as a designer his exquisite illustrations to Oscar Wilde's *The Sphinx* (1894) have a personal Art Nouveau elegance, and in his more exuberant work for the theatre he anticipated the richness and bold design of Léon Bakst.

Shannon's portrait of his companion, described on a label on the back of the frame as 'The Man in an Inverness Cloak', was painted two years after the foundation of the Vale Press (named after their house in Chelsea, offered to them by Whistler), when Ricketts was thirty-two. The linear approach was natural to an artist, who, up to about 1897, had worked chiefly in black and white, but the broad massing, strong silhouette, and lightly but carefully patterned grey background bear a striking resemblance to some of Whistler's celebrated portraits of a quarter of a century earlier (see p. 152), while the indeterminate shadow recalls Whistler's later backgrounds. Shannon had painted a Whistlerian self-portrait in 1897 and, although inventive and original in his later designs and poses, still composed a portrait of Wickham Steed in Whistlerian profile (National Portrait Gallery) as late as 1920.

Provenance: Sir Edmund Davis; purchased from the executors of Lady Davis by the NACF, and presented, 1942.

Literature: NACF Report, 1942, p. 15.

Jacques-Emile Blanche: *Charles Shannon and Charles Ricketts*
1904
Oil on canvas, 92.1 × 73 (36¼ × 28¾)
Tate Gallery, London

54

Anna Herkomer (Mrs Hubert von Herkomer)

Sir Hubert von Herkomer (1849–1914)

Oil on canvas, 51 × 61 (20 × 24)
Signed with initials b.l.: *HH* and dated upper right: *Aug 1876*

Watford Borough Council, Watford Museum Collection
(WM 3483)

Anna Weise (died 1882), Herkomer's first wife, was, like her husband, of German extraction; a prostrating attack of inflammation of the lungs, very soon after her marriage in 1873, developed into consumption, from which she eventually died.

Herkomer was aged eight when his Bavarian parents, his father a joiner and his mother a music teacher, settled in Southampton after six years in the United States. He entered the Southampton School of Art at the age of fourteen, studied briefly at the Munich Academy, and later trained at South Kensington, 1867–1868, where he came under the influence of Fred Walker. Working principally in watercolour, and as an illustrator of modern life subjects for the *Graphic* (founded 1869), but exhibiting on average one oil painting every year, he achieved fame overnight at the Royal Academy of 1875 with the perceived realism and pathos of *The Last Muster – Sunday at the Royal Hospital, Chelsea* (Lady Lever Art Gallery, Port Sunlight).

This portrait of his wife was painted for his own delight soon after the birth of their second child, Elsa. 'Through painting my dear wife's portrait and that of my beautiful Siegfried, I have at last some pictures for myself in the house', he wrote in September 1876; the picture, which was done at their home in Chelsea, is inscribed as 'painted for our dear children'. Unconventionally and charmingly composed, as if a camera had 'zoomed' in on the subject, the portrait is a loving and touching characterization, inevitably imbued with a deep sadness: Anna was already a semi-invalid. The picture has more in common with Herkomer's social realist subjects, where adversity or deprivation is tempered by a peasant fortitude, than with the colourful off-beat designs of James Tissot (whose wife also died of consumption), which it superficially resembles (see comparative illustration). Herkomer's portrait of their son Siegfried is also in the Watford Museum.

With increasing prosperity, but sadly not in Anna's lifetime, Herkomer was able to build at Bushey, where in 1883 he had founded the Herkomer School of Art, a fine house and studios for himself, where all his later work was executed (the only house in Britain to be designed by the great American architect, H.H. Richardson, whose portrait he had painted on his trip to the United States in 1885).

Provenance: Private Collection, Bushey; anon. sale, Christie's, 5 November 1982, lot 95; with David Messum, from whom it was purchased, 1984.

Literature: NACF Review, 1984, pp. 165–6.

James (Jacques Joseph) Tissot: *The Convalescent*
1872
Oil on wood, 37.5 × 45.7 (15 × 18)
Art Gallery of Ontario, Toronto
Gift of R. B. F. Barr, Esq., QC, 1966

55

Cecil Harrison

John Singer Sargent (1856–1925)

Oil on canvas, 172.8 × 83.6 (68 × 32⅞)
Exhibited at the Royal Academy, 1888, no. 314

Southampton City Art Gallery (485)

Cecil Harrison (1878–1915) was the eldest son of Robert Harrison, a wealthy stockbroker, and Helen, whose portrait by Sargent, exhibited at the Royal Academy of 1886, was regarded as one of his most magisterial images of fragile feminine beauty (see comparative illustration). Major Harrison, as he became, served in the Rifle Brigade and was killed on active service during the First World War.

Sargent studied in the atelier of Carolus-Duran, who laid the foundations of the young American's extraordinary technical facility with his insistence that his students should learn to paint touch by touch without reworking. Sargent worked in Paris with increasing acclaim at the Salon until the scandal associated with the décolletage and lavender flesh tints of his chic portrait of Mme X (which nonetheless he always regarded as the best picture he had ever painted) led him to settle in London in 1886.

During the mid-1880s Sargent was captivated with Impressionism (he stayed with Monet at Giverny in 1887) and the handling of his portrait of Cecil Harrison is in marked contrast to the hard-edged, somewhat brittle elegance of his Parisian portrait style, still characteristic of his painting of Helen Harrison. The youngster's pose is casual, thumbs in the pockets of his navy-blue sailor suit; the figure emerges from a shadowy, atmospheric though warm red background; and the hands are dissolved by the strength of the studio lighting by which the boy, his lips parted, seems mesmerized. The effect is one of 'intense vitality', as Claude Phillips noted in the *Academy* when the picture was exhibited.

Provenance: Presented by the sitter's mother, Mrs Robert Harrison, through the NACF, 1935.

Literature: NACF Report, 1935, p. 66; James Lomax and Richard Ormond in *John Singer Sargent and the Edwardian Age*, exh. cat., Leeds Art Galleries, National Portrait Gallery and Detroit Institute of Arts, 1979, no. 28.

John Singer Sargent: *Mrs Robert Harrison*
1886
Oil on canvas, 156.2 × 78.8 (61½ × 31)
Private Collection

56

Aubrey Beardsley

Walter Richard Sickert (1860–1942)

Oil (?tempera) on canvas, 76 × 31 (30 × 12¼)
1894
Signed b.l.: *Sickert*

Tate Gallery (4655)

Aubrey Beardsley (1872–1898) was a highly original but febrile draughtsman of strongly erotic inclinations, who made his name with his illustrations to Oscar Wilde's *Salome* and for the first volume of *The Yellow Book*, a periodical which, like so many avant-garde publications, including Ricketts's and Shannon's *The Dial*, only survived for a short time (April 1894 – April 1897). A leader of the 'aesthetic movement' which flowered in the nineties, Beardsley was closely linked with the world of Art Nouveau through his sinuous and artificial sense of pattern, which originated in his feeling for Japanese prints. He died of tuberculosis at the age of twenty-five.

Sickert was a pupil of Whistler, whom Beardsley revered, but gradually came to question the validity of his exquisite simplifications; more deeply aware than any other British artist of his generation of developments in contemporary French painting, he was certain that his friend, Degas, was 'the greatest painter of the age'. Reacting, too, against the conventions of beauty and sentiment imposed by the Royal Academy, Sickert, like Degas, drew most of his subjects during his long career from the commonplace events of lower middle-class life, and it was he whose example inspired the founding of the Camden Town Group in 1911; as Quentin Bell has written, 'all that was new and lively and progressive in British art tended to fetch up at 19, Fitzroy Street'. But Sickert was unconcerned with subject matter as such, or the titles which he afterwards devised – 'if the subject of a picture could be stated in words there had been no need to paint it' – and was obsessed rather with the underlying mood and with the problems posed by formal relationships, the solutions to which he would pursue in whole series of drawings and paintings.

In the early 1890s Sickert was still absorbed by the music hall (see comparative illustration), but was also painting landscapes and portraits. His portrait of Beardsley is closer to a figure study than a conventional portrait. In Wendy Baron's description, 'the face is hardly seen so that the whole figure is treated with equal emphasis ... The surface of the picture resembles a simple jigsaw of interlocking dry, flat, uniformly coloured and toned patches of paint'. Nonetheless it is an extraordinary evocation of the brilliant and dandified young draughtsman. The elongated format, enclosing the lanky figure, was one favoured by Sickert.

Sickert was never interested in conventional sittings, preferring, like Degas, to catch his subjects in a characteristic pose. His portrait of Beardsley is said to have been inspired by a circumstance at the unveiling of a memorial bust to Keats in Hampstead Church on 16 July 1894. After the ceremony

Beardsley took a short-cut, away from the crowd, by walking over the graveyard; his biographer, Haldane MacFall, recalled that 'there was something strangely fantastic in the ungainly efforts ... by the loose-limbed, lanky figure so immaculately dressed in black cut-away coat and silk hat, who carried his lemon-yellow kid gloves in his long white hands, his lean wrists showing naked beyond his cuffs, his pallid cadaverous face grimly set on avoiding falling over the embarassing mounds that tripped his feet'. The outlines of tombstones in the background of the picture lend credence to this account of its genesis, even if MacFall's vivid recollection was coloured by the painting itself (in which, however, the frock coat is grey not black and the gloves grey-blue not lemon-yellow). What seems inexplicable is that Sickert's portrait was reproduced that very month in the July 1894 issue of *The Yellow Book*, of which the young draughtsman was then the art editor. Possibly the issue appeared very late in the month, though even then the picture would have had to have been painted and reproduced at great speed. The painting is characteristically sombre in tone.

Provenance: The artist's mother, Mrs E.A. Beardsley; executor's sale, Sotheby's, 1932, bt. Tate Gallery.

Literature: Haldane MacFall, *Aubrey Beardsley, The Man and his Work*, 1928, p. xiii; NACF Report, 1932, p. 47; Mary Chamot, Dennis Farr and Martin Butlin, *The modern British paintings, drawings and sculpture*, vol. 2, Tate Gallery Catalogues, 1964, pp. 625–6; Wendy Baron, *Sickert*, 1973, p. 37 and no. 57; Kenneth McConkey, *Edwardian Portraits: Images of an Age of Opulence*, Woodbridge, 1987, no. 35.

Walter Richard Sickert:
Vesta Victoria at the Old Bedford
c. 1890
Oil on board, 36.8 × 23.5 (14½ × 9¼)
Private Collection

57

Self-portrait (Henry Tonks)

Henry Tonks (1862–1937)

Oil on canvas, 80.6 × 59.7 (31¾ × 23½)
Signed and dated b.l.: *HENRY TONKS 1909*

Tate Gallery (3231)

Henry Tonks (1862–1937) was trained as a surgeon and became senior medical officer at the Royal Free Hospital, Hampstead. A strong interest in art, fostered by part-time study with the great teacher, Frederick Brown, led him to abandon his surgical career when the latter offered him a teaching post at the Slade after his appointment as professor there in 1893. Among their early pupils were Augustus and Gwen John and William Orpen. In 1917 Tonks succeeded Brown as Head of the Slade School, but in the following year he was at the front working as a war artist with his close friend, Sargent (see comparative illustration). Tonks was the outstanding teacher of his age, though he drove his students hard, and tenaciously defended traditional academic values, notably fine draughtsmanship, against what he regarded as the onslaughts of modernism. As a painter he was unable to make up with dour tenacity for what he lacked in natural talent.

This self-portrait was painted when Tonks was living in Edith Grove, Fulham (he moved to Chelsea in the winter of 1910–1911). It is an elaborate academic exercise, incorporating, as in his best-known subject pictures, a complexity of shapes and effects of light. The influence of his lifelong friend, Wilson Steer, is abundantly evident. Space is carefully defined, the play of light and shade throughout is bold and naturalistic, and Tonks has subjected his head to a shaft of direct sunlight, placed his legs in difficult foreshortening and emphasized his large, workman's hands. It is an uneasy picture – Tonks is perched on the edge of his impractical painting armchair – and clumsily handled, but it is also something of a *tour de force*.

Hugh Hammersley, who presented this portrait to the Tate, was a wealthy banker who held artistic soirées at his house in Hampstead. Tonks, Steer, Augustus John and Sir William Rothenstein were among the habitués.

Provenance: Presented by Hugh Hammersley, through the NACF, 1917.

Literature: NACF Report, 1917, p. 16; Mary Chamot, Dennis Farr and Martin Butlin, *The modern British paintings, drawings and sculpture*, vol. 2, Tate Gallery Catalogues, 1964, p. 729; Kenneth McConkey, *Edwardian Portraits: Images of an Age of Opulence*, Woodbridge, 1987, no. 64.

John Singer Sargent: *Henry Tonks*
1918
Pencil and ink on paper, 24.8 × 37.1 (9¾ × 14⅝)
Fitzwilliam Museum, Cambridge

58

Augustus John

Sir William Orpen (1878–1931)

Oil on canvas, 99.1 × 94 (39 × 37)
Exhibited at the New English Art Club, 1900, no. 118

National Portrait Gallery, London (4252)

James McNeill Whistler:
Arrangement in Grey and Black, no. 2: Thomas Carlyle, 1872–1873
Oil on canvas, 170.2 × 142.2 (67 × 56)
Glasgow Museums and Art Galleries

Sir William Rothenstein: *Augustus John*, 1899
Oil on canvas, 77 × 56.2 (30 × 22)
The Board of Trustees of
the National Museums & Galleries on Merseyside,
Walker Art Gallery, Liverpool

Augustus John (1878–1961) entered the Slade School in 1894; following an unhappy childhood and a poor education, he was a timid and hard-working student, absorbed in the study of the Old Masters; Tonks called his work 'methodical'. On his summer holidays in 1897 John injured his skull when he struck a rock after diving into the sea; after his convalescence he came back to the Slade for the autumn term a changed being, flamboyant and unkempt in appearance, rebellious in attitude, mercurial in mood, above all, bold and virtuoso in his drawing. He became a legendary figure before he left the Slade and was Tonks's star pupil: Sargent thought his drawings the finest since the Italian Renaissance.

William Orpen entered the Slade in 1897, and won the coveted summer composition prize in 1899, the year after John had done so with his brilliant *Moses and the Brazen Serpent*: both their efforts were similarly eclectic in their derivation from the Old Masters. The two high-spirited young men were constant companions, travelled abroad together, and in 1903 collaborated in founding the Chelsea Art School. But John soon left Orpen to do the work at the school, and Orpen was too materially ambitious for John; their paths eventually diverged. Orpen, a sure draughtsman with a delight in accessory detail, went on to become the most prolific, successful and wealthy portrait painter of his day, working in a breezy and bravura style. Perhaps his most memorable works were his record of life at the front during the First World War.

Orpen made his debut at the New English Art Club with his portrait of John. Towards the end of his life the sitter recalled the portrait: 'Orpen had a cavernous studio in the basement [of 21 Fitzroy Street], where he once painted a most regrettable portrait of me. Having selected Whistler's 'Carlyle' for imitation (see comparative illustration), he posed me seated in profile against the wall, attired in a cast-off top-coat provided by Charles Conder. Unfortunately the result of his industry revealed no trace of the subtlety and distinction present in his exemplar.' John, who chiefly disliked the picture as showing the 'legend', the outer public persona rather than what he regarded as his true, dreamy, uncertain self (see comparative illustration), said that it was 'described in one notice as a clever portrait of Mr. John in the character of a French Romantic', and indeed John was at his most *farouche* at this time, just after he had left the Slade. For the *Times*, however, noticing Orpen for the first time, the portrait was 'admirably posed, full of expression, and drawn with great skill'. The pose, hat on knee, is indeed inspired by Whistler's celebrated portrait of Thomas Carlyle, but the image is substantial in volume rather than flattened into the plane, and the background contains warm reds which set off John's smouldering countenance; the strong lighting of the head, and especially the painterly treatment of the wrist and splayed fingers of the right hand, bear testimony to the pervasive influence of Rembrandt at this time, following the Rembrandt exhibition in Amsterdam in 1898, which John visited with Ambrose McEvoy, and the Winter Exhibition devoted to Rembrandt at Burlington House a few months later, in 1899. John's first Rembrandtesque self-portrait etching was made in about 1900.

Provenance: With Leicester Galleries, from whom it was purchased by the NACF, 1948, and lent to Swansea Art Gallery with a view to its being transferred to the National Portrait Gallery after the sitter's death; given by the NACF, 1962.

Literature: NACF Report, 1948, p. 32; Augustus John, *Finishing Touches*, 1964, p. 41; Bruce Arnold, *Orpen: Mirror to an Age*, 1981, pp. 73–4.

Orpen Dining Room Chair.
(Given to Billy, broken by Hannah?)

59

Winifred John

Gwen John (1876–1939)

Oil on canvas, 21.6 × 16.5 (8½ × 6½)
*c.*1895 (reproduced larger than actual size)

Tenby Museum and Picture Gallery

Winifred John (1879–1967) was the younger sister of Gwen John. The girls had two brothers, Thornton and Augustus (born 1878) (see nos. 58 and 64). The children had a strict Welsh upbringing, living first at Haverfordwest, in Pembrokeshire, then, after their mother's death in 1884, at Tenby, a pretty resort town on the other side of Pembroke. Winifred was a violinist, who emigrated to California in 1905 and became a violin teacher. One of her daughters, Muriel Matthews, described her in a letter to the Tenby Museum in 1971: 'Mother was a small, shy, and very gentle person who disliked crowds and abhorred publicity, but she was a most wonderful friend and companion ... She had a deep natural feeling and understanding for all the arts.'

Gwen John's portrait of her sister is the earliest known painting by her, presumably executed not long after she joined her brother, Augustus, at the Slade School in the autumn of 1895. Winifred seems to be aged about fifteen. The blouse and the warm background are loosely handled, but the characterization is sharp and sensitive. Augustus once told Whistler, who taught Gwen John at the Académie Carmen in Paris in 1898, that he thought his sister's work 'showed a feeling for character'. 'Character? What's that?' Whistler replied, 'It's *tone* that matters. Your sister has a fine sense of *tone*.' Gwen John made another, better-known portrait of Winifred about three years later, perhaps during the summer she spent in Tenby in 1898, between the Slade and Paris. There are also several drawings dating from the period 1895–1898, of which one is uncharacteristically flamboyant (see comparative illustration).

Provenance: Edwin John, the artist's father, who gave it to his housekeeper, Mrs Bessie Davies; passed to her great-niece, Mrs Melrose Norman, from whom it was acquired, 1971.

Literature: NACF Report, 1971, p. 34; Cecily Langdale, *Gwen John*, New Haven and London, 1987, no. 1.

Gwen John: *Winifred John in a Large Hat*
c. 1895–1898
Charcoal on paper, 31.1 × 24.1 (12¼ × 9½)
National Museum of Wales, Cardiff

60

Self-portrait (Gwen John)

Gwen John (1876–1939)

Oil on canvas, 61 × 37.7 (24 × 14⅞)
*c.*1900

National Portrait Gallery, London (4439)

Gwen John was trained at the Slade School, 1895–1898, then at the height of its reputation under the great teaching partnership of Brown and Tonks, and spent a few months at the newly opened Académie Carmen in Paris, where she was taught by Whistler. After four years painting in cheerless rooms in London, she returned to Paris, remaining there for the rest of her life and leading a modest and comparatively solitary existence, first in Montparnasse, then, from 1921, in the suburb of Meudon. She modelled for Rodin, with whom she had a long and passionate association, and later found a voracious patron in the American collector, John Quinn (who had given her brother, Augustus, a retainer in 1909); through him she met Braque, Picasso, Brancusi and other great contemporaries. By the 1920s she was well known to the Paris art establishment, and her work was regularly exhibited at the Salons. Her reticent *intimiste* style, which stemmed from Tonks and was influenced by Vuillard, embraced very few subjects: sparse interiors, still lifes, and, for the most part, female portraits, many of the same sitter, almost all anonymous. Dry and chalky in pigment, subdued in colour and tonally faultless, these later pictures were not strictly *of* anything or anyone; nonetheless (to Quinn's annoyance) she was apt to fuss over them endlessly. One model complained that 'she cannot endure having the pose changed by a hair's breadth after she has arranged it'.

Gwen John was about twenty-four, and living in London, when she painted this self-portrait. It is a remarkable image of self-confidence and rugged independence. Her hand firmly placed on her hip, she confronts the spectator from beneath her huge black bow, the rippling folds of her blouse breaking her loose from the confines of the picture frame. Gwynne-Jones wrote that he 'would rather possess the *Self-Portrait* than any other modern English portrait. It has grandeur, delicacy, most beautiful colour and, above all, intensity . . . her sensitiveness to tone is so great that it enables her to keep her colours very simple and very close together – this in effect gives a sense of grandeur to her smallest pictures'. The other, more restrained but no less beautiful, self-portrait Gwen John painted at this period (see comparative illustration) was a prized possession of her professor at the Slade, Frederick Brown.

Provenance: Augustus John; passed after his death to his wife, Dorelia, from whom it was purchased by the NACF, and presented (to mark Sir Alec Martin's eightieth birthday and forty years of service to the Fund), 1965.

Literature: Allan Gwynne-Jones, *Portrait Painters*, 1950, p. 34; NACF Report, 1965, p. 26; Cecily Langdale, *Gwen John*, New Haven and London, 1987, no. 8.

Gwen John: *Self-portrait in a Red Blouse*
1900–1903
Oil on canvas, 44.8 × 35 (17⅝ × 13¾)
Tate Gallery, London

61

Virginia Woolf

Vanessa Bell (1879–1961)

Oil on board, 40.7 × 30.5 (16 × 12)
1912

National Portrait Gallery, London (5933)

Virginia Woolf (1882–1941) was not only a remarkable novelist with a particular gift, as David Cecil wrote, for conveying 'the processes of unspoken thought and feeling', but one of the finest literary critics of her day. Cultivated and fastidious, she was the moving spirit behind the Bloomsbury circle and ethos. An intensely private person, Virginia Woolf had an almost pathological terror of sitting for her portrait. She refused to sit to David Bomberg; she refused more than once to be photographed by Cecil Beaton. She agreed to sit to the sculptor, Stephen Tomlin, in 1931, but gave up, in 'a state of rage and despair', after six short sittings. Tomlin's bust, sculpted in about 1935, is now recognized as one of the two most revealing likenesses of the great writer (see comparative illustration); as Quentin Bell wrote, it is 'far more like than any of the photographs . . . Virginia gave him no time to spoil his first brilliant conception'. The other is this tiny sketch by Virginia's sister, Vanessa.

Vanessa Bell made four sketches of Virginia Woolf during the course of weekends spent in Sussex in 1912. They show her in the year of her marriage to Leonard Woolf, and the year before her looks were greatly altered by one of her worst mental breakdowns, during which she attempted, nearly successfully, to commit suicide. The present study, suggestive of Virginia Woolf's nervous frailty, may have been made at Little Talland House at Firle. The bold handling and strong contours are characteristic of Vanessa Bell's first Post-Impressionist pictures, following the revelation of the Post-Impressionist exhibition at the Grafton Galleries in the winter of 1910–1911.

Provenance: T. Parsons; with Anthony d'Offay, from whom it was purchased, 1987.

Literature: Richard Shone, 'Virginia Woolf by Vanessa Bell', *Art at Auction*, Sotheby's, 1984–1985, pp. 58–62; NACF Review, 1988, p. 119.

Stephen Tomlin: *Virginia Woolf*
c. 1935
Lead cast of bust, 40.6 (16)
National Portrait Gallery, London

62

Dame Edith Sitwell

Alvaro Guevara (1894–1951)

Oil on canvas, 183 × 122 (72 × 48)
Exhibited at the International Society, 1919, no. 37

Tate Gallery (3509)

Edith Sitwell (1887–1964) was the eldest of the three children of Sir George Reresby Sitwell. Edith, Osbert and Sacheverell all became distinguished writers; Edith was primarily a poet. In 1916 she launched an annual anthology of new poems entitled *Wheels*, publishing in 1919 seven of Wilfred Owen's war poems. *Façade*, 1922, in collaboration with (Sir) William Walton, an agile, rhythmic and witty work, was a similar challenge to 'the rhythmical flaccidity, the verbal deadness, the dead and expected patterns, of some of the poetry immediately preceding us'.

Guevara was a Chilean artist who studied at the Slade; he subsequently worked at the Omega Workshops with Roger Fry and was influenced by Post-Impressionism. His portrait of Edith Sitwell, with its vertiginous high viewpoint (the rush mats are seen entirely from above) and impression of a corner of a room, is clearly influenced by the work of Degas (see comparative illustration), the doors and paintings on the walls in whose interiors are similarly cut by the picture frame. Stability is given to the canvas by Dame Edith's erect posture and the supporting verticals of the chair back and the architectural features behind her. Edith Sitwell's height, her pale, oval face, sharp nose and long fingers, and her characteristic flowing dress are strikingly emphasized in a pose that is contemplative – the eyes are almost closed, the loosely clasped hands suggestive of prayer – yet hints at latent energy. Gwynne-Jones admired 'the daring and brilliance of the setting from which the green dress shines out with multicoloured accents like the wings of a dragonfly ... the harmonizing element in the dazzling colour is its flicker.' When the portrait was exhibited at the International Society in 1919 it was entitled *The Editor of 'Wheels'*. This picture, and the similarly composed portrait of Nancy Cunard (National Gallery of Victoria, Melbourne), are perhaps Guevara's masterpieces.

Provenance: Presented by Sir Joseph Duveen (later Lord Duveen of Millbank), George Eumorfopoulos and Walter Taylor, through the NACF, 1920.

Literature: NACF Report, 1920, p. 31; Allan Gwynne-Jones, *Portrait Painters*, 1950, pp. 36–7; Mary Chamot, Dennis Farr and Martin Butlin, *The modern British paintings, drawings and sculpture*, vol. 1, Tate Gallery Catalogues, 1964, pp. 264–5.

Edgar Degas: *Diego Martelli*
1879
Oil on canvas, 110 × 100 (43½ × 39¾)
National Gallery of Scotland, Edinburgh

63

Admiral of the Fleet Lord Fisher of Kilverstone

Sir Hubert von Herkomer (1849–1914)

Oil on canvas, 172.7 × 119.4 (68 × 47)
Signed and dated b.l.: *H.H/1911*

National Portrait Gallery, London (2805)

'Jackie' Fisher (1841–1920) was a man of immense energy, foresight and originality of mind who became one of the greatest of British naval administrators, reformers and strategists at a critical period in the nation's history. In his early thirties he was closely involved with the development of a new weapon, soon to be an integral part of the naval arsenal, called the torpedo; as First Sea Lord, 1904–1910, he masterminded the creation of the dreadnought, an 'all big gun' fast battleship. He introduced sweeping reforms in naval training and concentrated the fighting efficiency of the Navy by the wholesale abolition of older ships and smaller dockyards overseas. Brought out of retirement in 1914, Fisher devoted his energies to the development of the submarine and a scheme for securing the command of the Baltic to make possible a military operation which would turn the German flank. He resigned over the Dardanelles adventure, 1915, which he thought ill-conceived, causing hideous losses and diverting the fighting strength of the fleet from the principal naval strategy of the war.

Herkomer, a painter of sentimental social realism influenced by Wilhelm Leibel and Bastien-Lepage as well as by Fred Walker, had made a considerable reputation as a portraitist by the 1880s (he needed the work to pay for the building of his grandiose house at Bushey), and was especially successful with large groups influenced by the civic portraiture of seventeenth-century Holland. Just as in his subject pictures his figures are images of dignity and fortitude, so in portraiture he sought the heroic and he painted Kitchener and Baden-Powell (both National Portrait Gallery) as well as *The Firm of Friedrich Krupp*, 1914.

Herkomer portrayed Fisher just after his retirement as First Sea Lord in his uniform as Admiral of the Fleet. There were probably only two sittings, conducted in 'a tremendous flow of conversation'. The immense column and the draped Union Jack tower over, though they do not dominate, the man. Nonetheless, in contrast to his portrait of Kitchener, intense and forbidding (see comparative illustration), Herkomer has stressed – by means of the smiling expression, the unruly forelock and the hand sunk in his jacket pocket – the charm and unconventionality rather than the ruthlessness of the great naval leader. It is an image of the admiral whose hero was Nelson, and who inspired younger officers not only through his vigour and love of experiment, but through his friendliness and his dislike of routine and the deadhand of senior service conservatism. The picture also exemplifies the range of cooler tones, with grey half-tones in the flesh tints, which Herkomer was developing at this time in place of his former reddish-brown tonality.

Provenance: Cecil, 2nd Baron Fisher, who presented it, through the NACF, 1936.

Literature: NACF Report, 1936, p. 57.

Sir Hubert von Herkomer:
Horatio Herbert Kitchener, 1st Earl Kitchener of Khartoum
1890
Oil on canvas, 139.7 × 109.2 (55 × 43)
National Portrait Gallery, London

64

Madame Suggia

Augustus John (1878–1961)

Oil on canvas, 186 × 165 (73½ × 65)
1920–1923. Exhibited at the Alpine Club, 1923, no. 12 (*Paintings and Drawings by Augustus John*), and afterwards at the *International Exhibition*, Carnegie Institute, Pittsburgh, 1924, no. 224

Tate Gallery (4093)

Thomas Gainsborough:
Anne Ford, later Mrs Thicknesse
1760
Oil on canvas, 196.9 × 134.6 (77½ × 53)
Cincinnati Art Museum, Cincinnati, Ohio
(Bequest of Mary M. Emery)

Guilhermina Suggia (1888–1950) was a celebrated Portuguese 'cellist, who had studied at Leipzig and later with Pablo Casals. From 1914 she lived in England, giving her last concert at the Edinburgh Festival in 1949.

Most of John's best work is brilliant and intuitive rather than complex and grand. Paradoxically, his overriding ambition, inspired by Puvis de Chavannes, was always to paint large murals; but again and again he was to show that he lacked the pictorial imagination and inventive power. The immense cartoon (Tate Gallery) for a commissioned canvas about the life of Galway City, 1916, is uninspired; and of his gigantic triptych of the gypsy pilgrimage to Les Saint-Maries de la Mer, which occupied him for the last twelve years of his life, Sir Charles Wheeler wrote that 'it became less and less resolved and was never finished'. John's *Lyric Fantasy*, 1911–1915 (Tate Gallery), was the most successful of his large works because it was founded on 'nature': on portraits of his own family and on the colourful, freely brushed oil sketches of landscapes that he was making at this period – works that are perhaps his most beautiful and original paintings.

After this brief moment of inspired creativity John's work steadily deteriorated, and in the 1920s and 1930s he did little else but commissioned portraits. Amongst these generally mediocre canvases his undoubted masterpiece, and perhaps his most famous painting, was *Madame Suggia*; but the effort was enormous. The work took three years. One canvas, in which the 'cellist wears a gown of blue sequins, was abandoned because it was not large enough. As always, John was seduced by scale. There were nearly eighty sittings; the colour of the gown was first gold and then white, before the present wine red was settled on; and John was constantly repainting, finding the positioning of the right arm particularly difficult. Madame Suggia played Bach throughout the sittings; 'sometimes', she recalled, John 'would begin to walk up and down in time to the music ... When specially pleased with his work, when some finesse of painting eyelash or tint had gone well, he would always walk on tiptoe'. The final design, based on crossing diagonals, and dominated by the 'cellist's magnificent sharp profile and taut, outstretched right arm, the cascading folds of the curtain behind echoing the tensed neck-bone, and the brilliantly orchestrated flounces of the voluminous gown sweeping down towards the frame, is magisterial. John had triumphed over his long struggle.

The picture invites comparison with the highly original bravura design of another portrait of a female musician painted two centuries earlier, Gainsborough's full-length of the viola da gamba player, Anne Ford (see comparative illustration). *Madame Suggia* was not completed in time for the Royal Academy exhibition of 1922, for which it had been planned; but it won first prize at the Carnegie International of 1924. A large oil sketch, in quite a different pose, is in the National Museum of Wales.

Provenance: William P. Clyde, Jr., New York, 1923, from whom it was purchased by Sir Joseph Duveen (later Lord Duveen of Millbank) and presented through the NACF, 1925.

Literature: NACF Report, 1925, p. 22; Mary Chamot, Dennis Farr and Martin Butlin, *The modern British paintings, drawings and sculpture*, vol. 1, Tate Gallery Catalogues, 1964, pp. 324–5; Malcolm Easton and Michael Holroyd, *The Art of Augustus John*, 1974, pp. 27 and 84; Michael Holroyd, *Augustus John*, 2 vols., 1975, vol. 1, pp. 94–5.

65

Sir Winston Churchill

Walter Richard Sickert (1860–1942)

Oil on canvas, 45.7 × 30.5 (18 × 12)
1927. Exhibited at the Savile Gallery, 1928, no.10

National Portrait Gallery, London (4438)

When this portrait of him was painted Winston Churchill (1874–1965) was Chancellor of the Exchequer in Stanley Baldwin's administration of 1924–1929 (he had thought when he was summoned that Baldwin was offering him the Chancellorship of the Duchy of Lancaster). An enthusiastic amateur painter, he had been taking lessons from Sickert (his wife's mother, Lady Blanche Hozier, had been a friend of Sickert in Dieppe).

Like Degas, Sickert habitually used photographs as an aid to his painting, and had done so all his working life. From about 1927, and for the rest of his career, he painted landscapes and theatre scenes as well as portraits with photographs, many of them press photographs rather than his own, as his direct source. Baron's impression of his probable method as far as portraits were concerned is that 'the sitter came to Sickert's studio, that Sickert painted the rough outline of his likeness and form onto the canvas in what seemed to him a characteristic pose, that he then had the sitter photographed in the same pose and worked thereafter mainly from the photograph.'

The portrait of Churchill was painted partly from life and partly from photographs; even the two pen and ink drawings which Sickert made may have been done from a photograph. One of these drawings is the same size as the painting; it was squared up, and the verso washed over with a thin coat of indian red, so that Sickert could trace it onto the canvas. The picture is painted entirely in tones of pink and greenish-blue. As in the case of his portrait of Beardsley, the image is greatly strengthened by the format, Churchill's pugnacious head seeming to break out of the tiny canvas, radiating boundless energy (see comparative illustration).

Provenance: The Hon. Baillie Hamilton; with Leicester Galleries, from whom it was purchased by Lady Pamela Berry (later Lady Hartwell), 1936; the Hon. Michael Berry (later Lord Hartwell) sale, Sotheby's, 12 July 1950, lot 138, bt. Malcolm on behalf of the NACF, and lent to the Ministry of Works with a view to its being transferred to the National Portrait Gallery after the sitter's death; given by the NACF, 1965.

Literature: NACF Report, 1950, p.26; Wendy Baron, *Sickert*, 1973, pp. 171, 174 and no. 403.

Augustus John: *Dylan Thomas*
c. 1936
Oil on canvas, 40.6 × 34.3 (16 × 13½)
National Museum of Wales, Cardiff
Heads as compelling as Sickert's image were among John's best work of the inter-war years.

66

Gwen Ffrangcon-Davies as Isabella of France: La Louve

Walter Richard Sickert (1860–1942)

Oil on canvas, 243.9 × 91.5 (96 × 36)
1932

Tate Gallery (4673)

Gwen Ffrangcon-Davies was born in 1896 and, trained as a singer, appeared with great success in Rutland Boughton's *The Immortal Hour*, 1920. She soon turned to the straight theatre, however, and her distinguished pre-war career ranged from Shakespeare's Juliet to Gwendolen in *The Importance of Being Earnest* and several acclaimed Shaw roles. In her later years she gave an appealing performance as Madame Voynitsky in Chekhov's *Uncle Vanya*, 1970.

After Sickert returned from Dieppe in 1922, following the death there of his second wife, he settled permanently in England, living first in Islington. In his later Islington years he went frequently to the theatre and a number of famous actors and actresses became his friends; Sickert had been a professional actor himself for three years after leaving college, and throughout his life he was a natural entertainer. In 1932 he painted, from a photograph published in the *Daily Sketch*, a portrait of Gwen Ffrangcon-Davies and himself arriving together at the Private View of the Royal Academy. Sickert painted the actress several times in various roles, and Ffrangcon-Davies told the compiler of the Tate Gallery Catalogue that Sickert had painted the present portrait from a photograph he particularly liked when he was looking through her albums. It had been taken by Bertram Park (whose name is included in the picture) at a dress-rehearsal of the Phoenix Society's production of Marlowe's *Edward II* in November 1923. The title *La Louve* (the she-wolf) was given to Isabella of France because of her ferocious character (see also comparative illustration).

The picture is by far the largest of Sickert's theatre subjects, and the canvas is squared-up for enlargement from the photograph. As in the case of his portraits of Beardsley and Churchill, the image is narrowly contained within the frame, giving a magical presence to the theatrically lit head and the massive weight of the white costume. The fact that the photograph had been taken nine years previously confirms Sickert's lack of interest in the image merely as a likeness.

Provenance: Exhibited at the Wilson Galleries, 1932, and there purchased by the NACF, the Contemporary Art Society and C. Frank Stoop through the Contemporary Art Society, and presented, 1932.

Literature: NACF Report, 1932, p. 23; Mary Chamot, Dennis Farr and Martin Butlin, *The modern British paintings, drawings and sculpture*, vol. 2, Tate Gallery Catalogues, 1964, pp. 626–7; Wendy Baron, *Sickert*, 1973, p. 176 and no. 416.

Walter Richard Sickert: *Gwen Again*
c. 1935–1936
Oil on canvas, 139.7 × 100.3 (55 × 39½)
Collection Bryan Ferry
This second portrait of Gwen Ffrangcon-Davies as Isabella of France is inscribed in Italian: 'The abuse heaped on the head of a king makes me speechless, makes me tremble'.

LA LOUVE

Index

The National Art Collections Fund

The National Art Collections Fund is Britain's premier art charity, helping all our museums to buy works of art to enrich their collections. Founded in 1903, our success has secured many of Britain's most important, and best-loved, works of art for our public collections.

In fact the NACF has saved over 10,000 works of art for the nation. We help museums and galleries all over the country, and we cover the whole range of the fine and decorative arts. Our first great triumph came when we bought Velázquez's *Rokeby Venus* for the National Gallery in 1905 for £45,000, then nine times the Gallery's annual purchase grant. And because of our work there are Monets in the Tate, Canalettos in Birmingham, Pre-Raphaelites in Bournemouth, as well as 400 teapots in Norwich and the legs of Henry VIII's armour in the Royal Armoury, to name just a few.

The National Art Collections Fund is an independent charity, and receives no government funding. We rely on members' subscriptions, bequests, and corporate donations to continue our work, and our role is becoming ever more vital as art prices soar and our museums are unable to keep pace. And we are a powerful voice urging the government to give better funding and a higher priority to the arts.

The NACF has over 30,000 members. Membership costs £15 a year, and benefits include free admission to all art museums and galleries in Britain, reduced admission to major exhibitions, and *The Art Quarterly*, our lively and informed magazine, mailed directly four times a year. We also produce a lavishly illustrated annual *Review* of our work, cataloguing everything we have helped to buy that year, which is also free to members. And, because our investments more than cover our running costs, every penny our members give us goes to buying works of art.

Join us, and help secure Britain's art heritage.

National Art Collections Fund:
20 John Islip St, London
SW1P 4JX.
Telephone: 071 821 0404.